ATLAS OF
Bacterial Flagellation

ATLAS OF
Bacterial
Flagellation

EINAR LEIFSON

*Stritch School of Medicine
of Loyola University
Chicago, Illinois*

ACADEMIC PRESS
New York and London
1960

Copyright ©, 1960, by Academic Press Inc.

ACADEMIC PRESS INC.
111 FIFTH AVENUE
NEW YORK 3, N. Y.

United Kingdom Edition
Published by
ACADEMIC PRESS INC. (LONDON) LTD.
40 PALL MALL, LONDON SW 1

Library of Congress Catalog Card Number 59-15755

PRINTED IN THE UNITED STATES OF AMERICA

Preface

The main purpose of this Atlas is to present a unified exposition showing the shape and arrangement of the flagella on representative strains of all available species of bacteria. The illustrations are all in the form of photomicrographs of stained preparations personally prepared by the author. In addition to the normal shapes and arrangements, the observed variations and mutations of flagellar shapes and arrangements are illustrated. Measurements of flagellar wavelengths and amplitudes were made on all cultures studied and these are recorded in the Atlas. With each genus is included the source of the cultures studied and a discussion of their authenticity and identity.

To enhance the practical value of the Atlas for bacteriologists, several chapters are included dealing with the various factors which influence bacterial motility and flagellation, technical details on the staining of flagella, and various methods by which flagellar variations and mutations may be studied.

Flagella are undoubtedly the locomotor organs of bacteria. Their composition is much the same as that of contractile tissue in general, such as muscle tissue. They are extremely thin, averaging only 20–30 millimicrons in diameter. The helical shape is most characteristic and most efficient for locomotion. The flagella originate from beneath the cell wall and perhaps from definite structures or kinetoplasts. How they operate to move the bacteria is not known, nor is the nature of the activating stimuli understood. Being locomotor organs, the shape of the flagella and their arrangement on the soma are determined by the genetic constitution of the bacteria.

Flagellation is a major basis for bacterial identification and classification. Because of technical difficulties experienced by many bacteriologists, the nature of the flagellation has been omitted from the original descriptions of many bacterial species. In some instances the flagellation has been incorrectly described. The Atlas should do much to rectify this situation and place morphology in its proper and preeminent place in bacterial taxonomy.

To the many bacteriologists throughout the world who have so generously contributed cultures the author expresses his sincere thanks.

Einar Leifson

Wheaton, Illinois
November, 1959

Contents

1. *Technical Problems Related to Motility and Flagellation*

THE BACTERIAL CULTURE

The synthesis of flagella and their activity does not always correlate with the other physiological activities of the bacteria. The environment which is best for growth and metabolism is not always best for flagellation and motility. Substances which have very minor effects on somatic growth and metabolism may completely inhibit flagellation or flagellar activity.

As a general rule flagellation is best in cultures incubated at relatively low temperatures such as 20° C. With some mesophilic bacteria little difference may be found in the flagellation observed at 20 and 37° C. With some genera, such as *Listeria,* the flagellation at 20° C. is good while that at 37° C. is very poor, and at 38° C. flagella are absent. In rare instances flagellation is better at higher temperatures than at lower temperatures. The only example the author can cite from personal experience is a culture of *Salmonella* in which both the flagellation and motility were distinctly better in cultures incubated at 37° C. as compared to 20° C. In many instances the apparently adverse effect of the higher temperatures of incubation is not due to the temperature as such, but rather to the growth phase in which the bacteria are examined. Overnight incubation at 37° C. of bacteria such as those of the enteric group, finds the bacteria long past the logarithmic phase and well into the death phase, while after the same length of incubation at 20° C. the bacteria are in a much more active state. After growth has ceased, the flagella may deteriorate more rapidly than the soma.

The optimum length of incubation for best flagellation seems directly related to the growth rate. In general it appears that the best flagellation is observed during the logarithmic and maximum stationary phases of growth. In one genus of bacteria, *Aeromonas,* the nature of the flagellation may change during the growth cycle. Strains of this genus may show numerous lateral flagella in young

1

cultures but only polar flagella in older cultures. This phenomenon has not been observed in other bacterial genera.

The chemical composition of the medium may greatly influence the flagellation. Of greatest importance perhaps is the pH. A low pH often has a distinctly deleterious effect on flagella. Fermentable carbohydrates should be omitted as much as possible and only added to the medium if necessary for growth. Phosphates appear to favor flagellation and the author routinely adds 0.1% potassium phosphate to his media. As a rule liquid media give better flagellation than solid media but sometimes the reverse seems to be true. For technical reasons, related to the staining procedure, the liquid medium used should be perfectly clear prior to inoculation. Any agar in the medium interferes with staining of the flagella. Satisfactory flagella stains may be made from thioglycollate cultures but better slides are obtained if the agar is omitted.

BACTERIAL MOTILITY

It is a good rule to examine the culture by moist preparation prior to staining. A motile culture should always show presence of flagella; if not, the staining technique is faulty. An apparently nonmotile culture may show presence of flagella for several reasons. The flagella may be in the "paralyzed" state; changes may have occurred in the medium, such as low pH, which have damaged the flagella; or the flagella may simply have ceased to function from various causes. Bacteria with flagella of the curly type are sometimes very poorly motile, and those with straight flagella are comparatively nonmotile. Another reason for making a moist preparation is that the nature of the motion indicates the nature of the flagellation. A single polar flagellum moves the soma rapidly and linearly without much, if any, wiggle. Peritrichous flagella move the bacteria with a characteristic wiggle. With a little experience polar and peritrichous flagellation are recognized with considerable accuracy. In a detailed study of the flagellation of the genus *Chromobacterium*, moist preparations of several strains showed linear motion characteristic of polar flagellation. However, the flagella stains showed only occasional lateral flagella which could not account for the motion observed. By modifying the stain

2

the polar flagella were finally visualized but would have been missed otherwise. Reliance cannot always be placed on spreading growth in semisolid or motility agar. Polar flagellated bacteria spread much less than the peritrichous flagellated, and if the flagellation is poor and polar, the culture may appear entirely nonmotile in the semisolid agar.

The simplest technique for making a satisfactory moist preparation is to place a loopful of culture on a slide and observe directly with low and high dry objectives. With proper adjustment of the condenser most bacteria may be seen. Light through a ground glass is better than light through a blue glass. The author uses a 20 × objective. For small bacteria, and poorly motile bacteria, a disk with an opaque center slipped into the condenser is very effective. Using the 10 or 20 × objective and the condenser all the way up, a very nice dark field may thus be obtained and even the slightest motion of the smallest bacteria detected. With low magnification the observer is less likely to mistake Brownian motion, and motion of convection currents, for vital motion.

STAINING OF FLAGELLA

Bacterial Suspension

If the bacteria are growing on a solid surface a light suspension is made in distilled water, taking care that only bacterial growth and none of the agar is carried into the suspension. For routine diagnostic purposes staining may be made directly from this suspension. Better preparations may be obtained by washing the bacteria. If the bacteria are pathogenic, formalin should be added to the suspension to a concentration of from 5 to 10%. The author routinely adds formalin to every suspension. Washing is accomplished as described for broth cultures.

If the bacteria are in broth culture, add 5–10% formalin, dilute with distilled water, mix and centrifuge; pour off supernatant and, while tube is still inverted, rinse lip of tube with distilled water to remove any supernatant which clings; now add 1–2 ml. of distilled water and shake to resuspend bacteria; dilute with distilled water, mix and recentrifuge; pour off supernatant as before, rinse lip of tube; suspend bacteria in 1–2 ml. of water and dilute to light sus-

3

pension. If the formalin is very acid it seems preferable to neu-
tralize it with sodium hydroxide. The final suspension should show
a barely visible turbidity.

To show the presence of pH-sensitive flagella the bacterial culture is divided into two tubes. Ten per cent dibasic potassium
phosphate is added to one tube to a concentration of 1%, and
10% monobasic potassium phosphate added to the other to a like
concentration. After mixing, formalin is added and the culture
washed as before. The flagella on some kinds of bacteria assume
the curly shape in the acid phosphate and the normal shape in the
alkaline phosphate.

The author has encountered only one group of bacteria which
is injured by distilled water, namely the red halophiles. These
bacteria completely dissolve in distilled water. They may be
washed in 20% sodium chloride solution but very successful
flagella stains of these bacteria were not obtained.

Preparation of Bacterial Smear

Clean and grease-free slides are essential for good stains. In
emergencies powdered cleansers such as Bon Ami may be used.
The author uses concentrated sulfuric acid saturated with potassium dichromate as cleaning solution. A strong solution of the
dichromate is first made in a relatively small quantity of water
and the sulfuric acid poured into this solution. If the cleaning solution is kept at room temperature the slides may require several
days to a week before they are clean. Greater efficiency is obtained
with hot solution, e.g., 70° to 80° C. In this temperature range
most slides are satisfactorily cleaned overnight. A glass rack for
holding the slides in the cleaning solution saves time and trouble.
When the slides have been cleaned they must be thoroughly
washed, first in tap water and then in distilled water, to remove
every trace of the acid. After washing they are dried by being
placed upright against a clean surface, such as a large beaker
placed on a paper towel. The dry slides are stored in a clean slide
box. The fingers must never touch any part of the slide to be used
for staining. It is a good practice to indicate on the storage box
which end of the slide has been handled and use the other end for
the staining. Just before use the slide is heated in the colorless
flame of a Bunsen burner (the side to be used against the flame)
and then laid on a piece of paper, to prevent cracking, until cool.

4

If the burner has a pilot light this must be turned off or the flame will be smoky. A smoky or yellow flame ruins the slide. On prolonged storage the slides may become greasy and must be re-cleaned. In the atmosphere of a large industrial city this may occur in a few weeks.

Sulfuric acid cleaning solution, if hot, gives off appreciable amounts of sulfur oxides which may ruin the flagella stains. Remove all hot cleaning solution from the vicinity of the staining place, preferably to another room.

Draw a line with a wax pencil transversely across the middle of the slide. Be sure the pencil line reaches both edges. A heaping, medium size loopful of the prepared suspension is placed on the distal end of the cool or slightly warm slide; the slide is tilted to cause the liquid to run down to the wax line. If the liquid does not run down readily the slide is not clean and results may not be good. Two smears, side by side, are readily made on each slide. The smear is allowed to dry in air and not fixed in any manner. It is now ready to be stained.

Preparation of Flagella Stain

The stain formula given below has proven satisfactory for the visualization of the flagella of all bacteria with a few exceptions such as the polar flagella of some strains of *Chromobacterium*. The latter may be visualized by doubling the concentration of tannic acid in the stain, i.e., instead of using a stock solution of 3% tannic acid use a stock solution of 6% tannic acid. With the higher concentration of tannic acid the staining time is longer, close to double. The normal formula of each stock solution is as follows:

Basic fuchsin in 95% ethyl alcohol, 1.2%; tannic acid in distilled water, 3.0%; sodium chloride in distilled water, 1.5%.

The basic fuchsin may be purchased certified for flagella staining. It should either be pure pararosaniline acetate or a mixture of pararosaniline hydrochloride and pararosaniline acetate, but not over $\frac{2}{3}$ parts of the hydrochloride. Basic fuchsin must have an odor of acetic acid to be satisfactory. Allow about 1 day to insure complete solution of the fuchsin.

The tannic acid should preferably have a light yellow color. To prevent molds from growing in the tannic acid solution addition of phenol to a concentration of about $\frac{1}{2000}$ is effective. The tannic acid and the sodium chloride solutions may be mixed with equal parts of each or prepared as one solution with 1.5% tannic acid and 0.75% sodium chloride. The stock solutions should be kept in the refrigerator.

To prepare the stain, mix together equal parts of the three stock solutions, or add 2 parts of the tannic acid-salt solution to 1 part of the dye solution. Keep the stain bottle tightly stoppered. The stain is ready for use immediately. A precipitate develops in the bottle on storage which should not be disturbed when the stain is used. The stain solution undergoes a gradual change during storage, requiring a longer staining time; the change is faster at higher temperatures. At room temperature the stain solution is satisfactory for about 1 week, in the refrigerator for 1–2 months, and in the deep freeze indefinitely. If the stain is frozen, care must be taken to mix thoroughly after thawing, since the alcohol has separated from the water. The author keeps his stain solution in the refrigerator and discards it when the staining time exceeds that of the freshly prepared stain by more than about 5 minutes.

Application of the Stain

For application of the stain solution the slides are most conveniently placed on a board or rack. The author uses a board, painted or stained black, about 3 inches wide and 20 inches long with very short legs slightly higher in front than in back. This gives a slight tilt to the board and the slides, and the staining solution is slightly deeper at the distal end of the slide than in the middle. With a Pasteur pipette, fitted with a rubber bulb and marked at the 1-ml. level, 1 ml. of the stain is taken from the top of the solution and is quickly applied to part of the slide holding the smear. The stain solution must not spread beyond the wax line or run off the slide.

Staining Time

The time required for staining the flagella varies normally between 5 and 15 minutes. A short staining time is required with freshly prepared stain, warm stain, high room temperature, strong air currents, thin stain layer, and pure pararosaniline acetate dye. A longer staining time is required with old stain solutions, cold stain, cold room, little air circulation, deep stain layer, and high

6

proportion of pararosaniline hydrochloride in the dye. When the alcohol has evaporated to concentration of 20–25% a colloidal precipitate forms which settles on the flagella making them thicker and colored red. Freshly prepared stain usually has a variable amount of coarse precipitate. On storage in the refrigerator this precipitate settles and the supernatant used for staining is clear. Do not disturb this precipitate when removing stain from the bottle. By careful observation of the stain on the slide the formation of the colloidal precipitate may be observed by the change from a clear solution to an opaque and rust colored solution. With the slide on a black background a strong beam of light readily shows the formation of this precipitate. As soon as the precipitate has formed the staining is completed and the slides are washed immediately.

Another method is to prepare one or two extra slides. When the staining time appears to be about up the trial slide is washed. If the smear is not macroscopically visible the time is too short. After about 2 more minutes wash off the second slide and observe the smear. With a little experience one trial slide is usually sufficient and will serve as a guide to the staining time of a dozen or more slides stained at the same time. When many slides are stained at one time they should be placed on the board about 1 inch apart to allow the alcohol to evaporate at somewhat the same rate from the middle and end slides. When the staining time is up the slide is placed directly under the faucet or a stream of water. Do not allow any of the stain to run off the slide before it is placed under the faucet. After washing, the slide is allowed to drain dry or carefully blotted.

Counterstaining

The soma of some species of bacteria characteristically stain very faintly or not at all. With such organisms a counterstain may be used for better visualization of the soma. A satisfactory counterstain is the usual methylene blue stain diluted 5–10 times with water and slightly alkalinized with sodium hydroxide, sodium bicarbonate, or sodium borate. Application of this stain for a minute or so usually stains the soma blue while the flagella remain red.

7

2. Shape and Arrangement of Flagella

FLAGELLAR SHAPE

The most common shape of bacterial flagella is a fairly uniform helix with a pitch characteristic of the species. Since the flagella are very thin the helix is flattened when they dry on the slide and they appear to be wavy. The distance from one wave crest to the next, which is termed the wavelength, may be slightly different from the pitch of the original helix, but measurements made on stained flagella and on flagella in moist preparation (dark field) have shown little difference. The amplitude of the waves is comparable to the diameter of the original helix. The exact relationship of these two is still somewhat uncertain but the amplitude seems definitely greater than the diameter of the helix. With most bacteria the flagellar shape is quite uniform and constant, but with a few bacteria the flagellar shape is quite irregular.

Measurement of flagellar wavelength and amplitude is most conveniently and accurately done by means of a filar micrometer. A fixed scale micrometer is less accurate but gives good mean values where many flagella are measured. Since some flagella are bound to become damaged and distorted when they dry on the slide, such flagella should not be measured. Figure 1 illustrates the way in which wavelength and amplitude are defined.

FLAGELLAR ARRANGEMENT

The old terminology describing the arrangement of the flagella on the bacterial soma is rather inadequate. The following terminology will be used throughout this Atlas:

Polar. (*a*) Monotrichous: Predominantly a single flagellum at one or both poles. The base of the flagellum usually parallel to the long axis of the soma. (*b*) Multitrichous:[1] Predominantly two or

---

[1] Since this classification is based primarily on flagellar arrangement the term lophotrichous is not included. Where this term is used in the Atlas it refers to polar multitrichous flagellation with flagella of relatively long wavelength and typically having less than one complete wave.

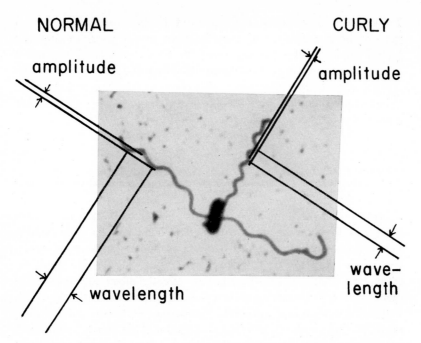

NORMAL

CURLY

amplitude

amplitude

wavelength

wave-
length

FIG. 1. Illustration of the way that wavelength and amplitude are defined. From E. Leifson, S. R. Carhart, and M. Fulton, *J. Bacteriol.* **69**, 73-82 (1955).

more flagella at one or both poles. The base of the flagella usually parallel to the long axis of the soma.

Subpolar. (*a*) Monotrichous: Predominantly a single flagellum near the pole with the base of the flagellum usually at a right angle to the long axis of the soma. (*b*) Multitrichous: Several flagella near the pole with the base of the flagella usually at a right angle to the long axis of the soma.

Lateral. (*a*) Monotrichous: A single flagellum predominantly from the middle half of the soma. (*b*) Multitrichous: Several flagella as a tuft predominantly from the middle half of the soma.

Peritrichous: Flagella seemingly haphazardly arranged on the soma, either single or multiple.

Mixed: Two or more flagella of distinctly different appearance in different locations.

The subpolar arrangement is rare. The monotrichous type has been seen mainly in *Rhizobium,* the multitrichous type only in

9

Treponema. The lateral arrangement is also rare. The lateral monotrichous arrangement may be seen in *Lachnospira* and the lateral multitrichous arrangement in *Selenomonas*. The mixed arrangement is typical of *Chromobacterium* and young cultures of *Aeromonas*. It has also been observed on several occasions, in cultures physiologically related to *Pseudomonas*, and in unstable mutants of various bacteria. (See Figs. 2 and 3.)

RELATION OF SHAPE AND ARRANGEMENT TO MOTILITY

In a liquid medium bacteria with polar flagella as a rule move more rapidly than bacteria with peritrichous flagella. The movement of the polar flagellated bacteria is linear and smooth, while that of the peritrichous flagellated bacteria is wiggly and more erratic. The shape of the flagella may greatly affect locomotor efficiency and will be discussed in the next section in connection with flagellar variation and mutation. In media with more solidity than ordinary broth the peritrichous flagellated bacteria apparently move faster than the polar flagellated bacteria. This is readily demonstrated by inoculating the center of one semisolid plate with a peritrichous organism such as *Salmonella,* and similarly inoculate another semisolid plate with a polar organism such as *Pseudo-*

Fig. 2. a, b, c, d, e, f, g. Examples of polar monotrichous flagellation, illustrating variations of wavelength.

h. This illustrates the formation of two variants, one with a normal flagellum and one with an undulant flagellum.

i. A normal and a straight flagellum at the same pole.

j, k, l, m, n, o. Various types of polar multitrichous and lophotrichous flagellation. The coiled flagella shown in o are quite rare.

p. Subpolar monotrichous flagellation.

q. Subpolar multitrichous flagellation.

r. Lateral monotrichous flagellation.

s. Lateral multitrichous flagellation.

t, u. In t is shown a stalked organism with a flagellum at the end of the stalk. In u is shown a rosette of stalked bacteria with polor monotrichous flagellation.

g, k, q. From E. Leifson, *J. Bacteriol.* 62, 377-389 (1951). j. From E. Leifson, *Antonie van Leeuwenhoek, J. Microbiol. Serol.* 20, 102-110 (1954). m, o. From E. Leifson, and R. Hugh, *J. Bacteriol.* 65, 263-271 (1953). p. From E. Leifson, and E. W. Erdman, *Antonie van Leeuwenhoek, J. Microbiol. Serol.* 24, 97-110 (1958).

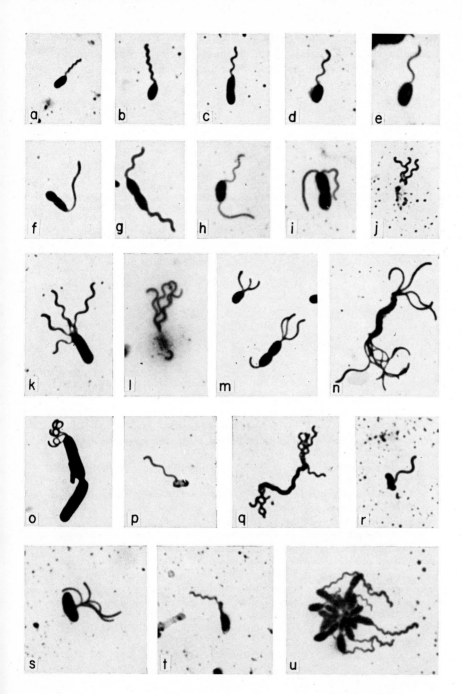

monas. The *Salmonella* growth will spread faster and more widely than the *Pseudomonas* growth. In fact, semisolid agar stabs of polar flagellated organisms may show so little spreading that they appear nonmotile.

Fig. 3. a, b, c, d, e, f. The variety of peritrichous flagella which have been observed and are named in order, normal, curly, small amplitude, coiled, semicoiled, and straight.

g, h. Two examples of double curvature. Other types, not illustrated, may be seen in *Proteus.*

i, j. Examples of peritrichously flagellated bacteria with flagella of different wavelength on the same individual.

k, l, m. Mixed polar-peritrichous flagellation.

n. The hooked flagellum is the normal one for this organism and is sub-polar in origin. The exact origin of the other flagella is undetermined.

o. Mixed lophotrichous-peritrichous flagellation. This is an unstable mutant.

p. The nature and function of the spine-like structures is unknown. The polar flagellum is unusually long but otherwise normal.

a, b, e, h, i. From E. Leifson, S. R. Carhart, and M. Fulton, *J. Bacteriol.* **69**, 73-82 (1955). c. From E. Leifson, and M. I. Palen, *J. Bacteriol.* **70**, 233-240 (1955). k. From E. Leifson, *J. Bacteriol.* **71**, 399-400 (1956). l. From E. Leifson, and R. Hugh, *J. Bacteriol.* **65**, 263-271 (1953). n. From E. Leifson, and L. W. Erdman, *Antonie van Leeuwenhoek, J. Microbiol. Serol.* **24**, 97-110 (1958). o. From T. P. Galarneault, and E. Leifson, *Can. J. Microbiol.* **2**, 102-110 (1956).

12

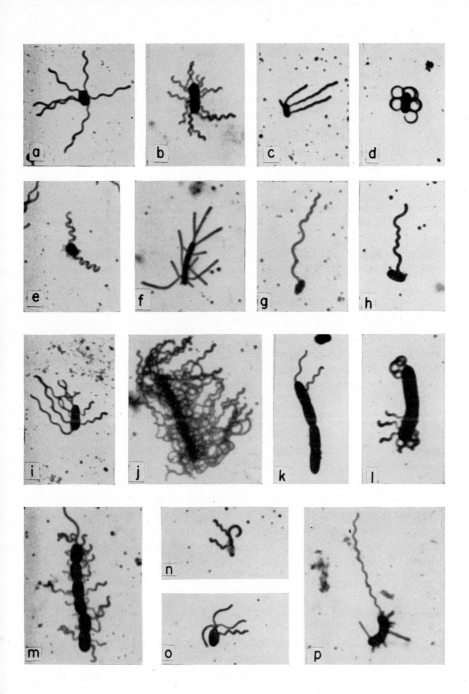

13

3. *Variation and Mutation of Flagellar Shape, Arrangement, and Function*

VARIATION OF SHAPE

Flagella may show several shape variations which are encountered with variable frequency in a variety of genera. The shape most usual for the flagella of a genus is designated as normal. This shape is usually that of a helix with a wavelength-amplitude ratio ranging from 4:1 to 3:1.

The most commonly encountered shape variant is the curly. This shape variant has been observed in most genera of peritrichous flagellated bacteria but infrequently in polar flagellated bacteria. In the enteric and related groups of bacteria, the curly flagella have a wavelength close to $\frac{1}{2}$ that of the normal. The ratio of wavelength to amplitude approximates 3:1 while in the normal for these bacteria this ratio approximates 4:1. In other groups of bacteria such as *Bacillus* and *Clostridium* the wavelength of the curly flagella is about $\frac{1}{3}$ that of the normal flagella. In the subpolar types of *Rhizobium* the curly flagella have a wavelength about $\frac{1}{4}$ that of the normal. In one strain of *Sarcina urea* three wavelengths were observed having a relative ratio of 3:2:1. The curly flagella appear shorter and stiffer than the normal. From a careful study of the two types of flagella in *Proteus* the actual lengths of the normal and the curly flagella when stretched out straight appeared to be about the same. In some strains of some genera of bacteria the change from normal to curly and vice versa may be induced by a change of the pH of the suspending medium. Strains of *Proteus, Azotobacter, Erwinia,* and *Bacillus* have shown this phenomenon. At pH 6 and below, the flagella are curly while at pH 7 and above they are normal. In these genera, as well as in others which do not show this pH sensitivity, both normal and curly flagella may appear on the same soma. In some genera or species the curly flagella appear to be stable genetic mutants. Curly flagella are less efficient locomotor organs than normal flagella. A pure curly strain of *Salmonella wichita*, for example, showed prac-

14

tically no spreading in semisolid agar and only wiggling and spinning motion in liquid media.

Next to the curly the most common variant is the coiled type. The flagella of one genus of bacteria, *Serratia,* are mainly coiled. The coiled shape may be the flattened appearance of a helix with a very large amplitude and short wavelength. This shape is fairly frequent in many genera of both peritrichous and polar bacteria but it is rare to find a culture which shows only coiled flagella. Aside from *Serratia,* cultures showing only coiled flagella have been found in *Aeromonas, Listeria* (true mutant), *Escherichia,* and *Erwinia.* Locomotor efficiency of coiled flagella is fair but less than that of normal flagella.

Other shape variations less frequent than those mentioned are straight, small amplitude, and undulant. Straight flagella are occasionally seen among the normal flagella of many bacteria. Pure variants or mutants with straight flagella are rare. Stable variants with straight flagella have been isolated from several cultures of *Listeria.* One strain of *Arthrobacter* studied had mainly straight flagella. Organisms with straight flagella are either nonmotile or show only a nonprogressive spin or wiggle. Both types have been observed in *Listeria.*

Organisms with small amplitude flagella have been observed in *Listeria, Sarcina, Rhizobium,* and occasionally in other genera. Pure variants with this type of flagella have been isolated from *Listeria* strains. The motility of these variants was poor and practically nonprogressive, like organisms with straight flagella.

The undulant type of flagella was observed on one strain of *Thiobacillus thioparus,* on several strains of halophilic *Pseudomonas* species, and on several strains of *Aeromonas.* This is the type of flagella found on algae, such as *Chlamydomonas,* on protozoa, and apparently on flagellated plant gametes. With the single exception of a peritrichous organism seen in water all undulant flagella seen have been polar.

VARIATION OF FLAGELLAR ARRANGEMENT

Variation of flagellar arrangement is relatively rare but has been observed in several genera. The variation is always from polar flagellation or subpolar flagellation to peritrichous flagellation, never the reverse. This seems to indicate to the author an evolutionary trend in bacteria from polar flagellation to peritrichous flagellation. Typical strains of the *Aeromonas* genus show predominantly polar monotrichous flagellation in cultures which have attained a relatively dense population. In very young or very light cultures several strains showed peritrichous flagellation in addition to the polar. The lateral flagella usually have a shorter wavelength than the polar flagellum. Although the polar flagellum may be of the normal or undulant type the lateral flagella are alike. One widely distributed strain, indistinguishable from *Aeromonas* physiologically, has coiled peritrichous flagella and appears to be a stable mutant. A well authenticated mutation has been observed in a strain of *Lophomonas*. *Lophomonas* has polar multitrichous flagella of long wavelength like the spirilla. In one culture typical of the genus, lateral flagella of relatively short wavelength were observed in addition to the typical polar flagella. Individuals with only peritrichous flagella were also observed. The latter were isolated in pure culture and have remained unchanged over a period of years. This culture is indistinguishable from typical *Alcaligenes* species with curly flagella. In several strains of *Rhizobium* with a single subpolar flagellum, occasional individuals with one or more subpolar or lateral flagella of very short wavelength have been observed. Most often the normal subpolar flagellum and the curly flagella are found in the same individual, but occasionally organisms are seen with only the curly flagella. Pure variants of *Rhizobium* with only the curly flagella have not been isolated.

VARIATION IN MOTILITY

The change in motility associated with change of flagellar shape has been discussed. Yet to be mentioned is the complete absence of motility observed in some strains with otherwise normal flagella. This phenomenon has been observed in *Salmonella* and *Listeria*. These "paralyzed" mutants have shown fair stability.

Flagellar variants of bacteria which show differences in motility may be isolated by plating in semisolid agar. The most convenient technique is to streak plates of solid agar with the culture and a thin layer (about 7 ml. for a 15 cm. plate) of semisolid agar (0.3–0.5% agar) poured on top. Sometimes better results are gotten by making proper dilutions of the culture and inoculating the melted semisolid agar before it is poured on the solid agar. Plates made by either of these two methods can be turned over and otherwise handled like ordinary solid agar plates. Colonies of bacteria with normal peritrichous flagella tend to spread most widely. Colonies of bacteria with peritrichous flagella of any other shape tend to spread less widely, if at all. Colonies of polar flagellated bacteria with normal flagella spread less widely than those of peritrichous flagellated bacteria with normal flagella.

Detection of spontaneous mutants with greater motility than the parent strain is best accomplished by making a heavy streak across the middle of a solid agar plate followed by a thin layer of semisolid agar. Mutants with greater motility than the parent strain show up after a variable length of incubation (up to 20 days) as outshoots from the main streak.

4. Bacterial Evolution with Respect to Flagellation

The available evidence indicates that bacterial evolution is from polar monotrichous organisms to peritrichous organisms and, finally, to atrichous organisms. Polar flagellation is most efficient for locomotion through a liquid medium and such bacteria are best adapted to an aquatic habitation. All strictly autotrophic bacteria, and most water types, both fresh water and marine, have shown only polar flagellation, if any. Current ideas on the evolution of the earth are that in the early stages the surface was completely covered with water. In this environment the polar flagellated bacteria were evolved. Peritrichous flagellated bacteria are more efficient in locomotion through a medium denser than water and, as more and more land appeared, the peritrichous types evolved in the soil. With the appearance of animals and plants some bacteria became parasitic with an environment in which flagella served no useful purpose and were only a hindrance in that they required food and energy to be produced and to function. Under these conditions the bacteria evolved into atrichous types. Soil, and even water, rich in bacterial food could also render flagella superfluous.

Flagellar variations and mutations which have been observed in the laboratory invariably have been changes from polar flagellation to peritrichous flagellation, never the reverse, and from peritrichous to atrichous, rarely the reverse. An unequivocal instance is a polar flagellated strain of *Lophomonas* which spontaneously mutated to a peritrichous type. Strains of *Aeromonas* produce peritrichous cells in young cultures, and indirect evidence indicates that one *Aeromonas* culture produced a stable peritrichous mutant. There are some indications that the subpolar flagellated *Rhizobium* species of soy bean, lima bean, lupine, etc. are evolving into peritrichous types. The *Rhizobium* species from pea, garden bean, alfalfa, clover, etc. have peritrichous flagella, indicating perhaps a longer period of association with plants and rich soil.

The evidence for the peritrichous to the atrichous type of evolution is very suggestive. The mutation of laboratory cultures from peritrichous to atrichous is common experience. A majority of the bacteria strictly parasitic and pathogenic for animals are atrichous.

The flagellated pathogenic types are mainly intestinal where conditions favorable to peritrichous flagellation may exist to some extent. The plant pathogens, however, are generally flagellated, both polar and peritrichous. This may indicate that much of their existence is in water and soil. Instances of mutations from non-flagellated to flagellated types appear to be very rare and have never(?) been observed in genera other than those which have some species which normally are flagellated.

5. *Nitrosomonas*

A culture labeled *Nitrosomonas europaea* was received from Dr. Martin Alexander of Cornell University. Dr. Alexander stated that the culture was not pure and that attempts at purification had not been successful. Another culture with the same label was obtained from the American Type Culture Collection (ATCC).

FLAGELLAR CHARACTERISTICS

Stains were made directly from the broth culture furnished by Dr. Alexander. Two types of flagellated bacteria were seen. Most numerous was a small rod with polar monotrichous flagellation. The wavelength of the flagellum was exceptionally short averaging 0.93 micron. A much smaller number of rod shaped organisms had polar monotrichous flagella of much greater wavelength, averaging 2.3 microns, or about $2\frac{1}{2}$ times the other one. The soma of the organism with the long wavelength flagellum did not take the flagella stain and was practically invisible. The author did not plate or attempt to grow the Alexander culture in the proper synthetic medium. However a transfer was made into peptone-yeast extract broth, and growth appeared. This growth had a pinkish-brown color, water insoluble; flagella stain showed polar monotrichous flagella of 2.2 micron wavelength. Morphologically the organism was similar to the one with the long wavelength seen in the original culture. The real *N. europaea* would thus seem to be the type with the short wavelength flagella illustrated in Fig. 4a.

The ATCC culture of *N. europaea*, 12248 was stained directly from the original suspension. The predominant flagellation was polar monotrichous, with a smaller proportion of polar multitrichous individuals. The flagellar wavelength was rather variable ranging from 1.3 to 1.6 microns. On transfer to nutrient broth good growth was obtained of organisms with the same flagellation found in the original suspension. No growth was obtained in media free from organic matter. This organism apparently is not autotrophic and not typical of *Nitrosomonas*.

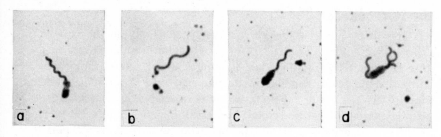

Fig. 4. a. *Nitrosomonas europaea,* Alexander strain.   Polar monotrichous flagellation. Note the very short wavelength.

b. *Nitrosomonas* (?) sp., Alexander strain. Polar monotrichous flagellation. Note the relatively long wavelength. This organism is not autotrophic and probably not a *Nitrosomonas* sp.

c, d. *N. europaea* (?), ATCC 12248. The organisms shown in c and d are typical examples of the organisms in the culture studied. Since the culture was not strictly autotrophic the organisms shown are probably not *Nitrosomonas.*

6. *Nitrobacter*

Only one culture labeled *Nitrobacter* was obtained, namely *Nitrobacter agilis*, ATCC 12812 (Fig. 5). The original liquid culture did not show motility, but staining showed a fair proportion of the bacteria with flagella. The organisms were very small, often coccoid, with a single flagellum which was not polar. The flagellation is perhaps best described as lateral monotrichous. Further study of this organism should be made to be sure it is not peritrichous.

7. *Hydrogenomonas*

Two cultures labeled *Hydrogenomonas* were studied: *Hydrogenomonas pantotropha* NRRL, B-935 and *Hydrogenomonas facilis*, ATCC 11228 (Fig. 6). The first of these was nonflagellated. *H. facilis* was well flagellated with polar monotrichous flagella of average wavelength of 1.8 microns. The wavelength was quite variable ranging from 1.3 to 2.2 microns.

8. *Thiobacillus*

Two species of the genus *Thiobacillus* were studied, namely, *Thiobacillus thiooxidans* and *Thiobacillus thioparus* (Fig. 7). A strain of each species was received from Dr. Robert Starkey of Rutgers University, and a strain of each species from Dr. J. D. Stout of the Ministry of Agriculture in New Zealand. The Starkey strains were isolated from soil in the United States. The Stout strain of *T. thiooxidans* was isolated from the water of a hot spring in New Zealand and the *T. thioparus* strain from New Zealand soil. The four strains appeared to be strict autotrophs but further identification was not made by the author.

FLAGELLAR CHARACTERISTICS

The two *T. thiooxidans* cultures were very similar, with normal polar monotrichous flagella. The Starkey culture of *T. thioparus* appeared nonmotile and flagella could not be demonstrated. The Stout culture of *T. thioparus* showed undulant polar monotrichous flagella, often at both ends. No distinct variants were observed in any of the cultures.

The wavelength of *T. thiooxidans* averaged 1.63 microns with amplitude of 0.55 micron. The wavelength of *T. thioparus* could not be measured accurately but was about 4.0 microns.

22

Fig. 5. a. *Nitrobacter agilis*, ATCC 12812. The organism illustrated shows the typical flagellation of the individuals in the culture studied. The flagellation may be labeled lateral monotrichous.

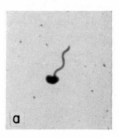

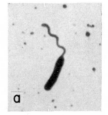

Fig. 6. a. *Hydrogenomonas facilis*, ATCC 11228. Polar monotrichous flagellation.

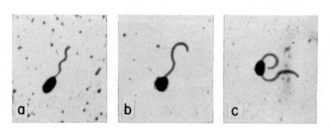

Fig. 7. a. *Thiobacillus thiooxidans* showing a typical normal polar monotrichous flagellum. b and c. *Thiobacillus thioparus* showing undulant polar monotrichous flagella.

9. *Pseudomonas*

The genus *Pseudomonas* has a large number of species many of which are inadequately described and appear to be unobtainable from any source. By definition, all motile strains of the genus must have polar flagella, either polar monotrichous or polar multitrichous. Physiologically the most typical members of the genus oxidize, but do not ferment, carbohydrates. Polar monotrichous or multitrichous heterotrophic bacteria which ferment carbohydrates with acid formation are better classified as *Vibrio* or *Aeromonas*. Still included in the genus are polar flagellated bacteria which have no effect on carbohydrates. These are often mistakenly labeled *Alcaligenes*. The genus *Lophomonas* has been suggested for a polar multitrichous or lophotrichous type which does not attack carbohydrates. The type species, *Pseudomonas aeruginosa,* produces a water soluble greenish pigment, but many otherwise typical species do not produce the pigment. For practical reasons the genus will be discussed under three headings: (1) The ordinary pseudomonads of fresh water, soil, and animal body; (2) the plant pathogens; (3) the halophilic types.

CULTURES

More than one hundred strains of the ordinary *Pseudomonas* from fresh water, soil, and the animal body were studied. These were obtained from a variety of sources over a period of several years. Among the major sources were Dr. W. D. Haynes of the United States Department of Agriculture (U.S.D.A.); Dr. MacDonald Fulton, Stritch School of Medicine; William Keller of Philadelphia; the Illinois State Health Laboratory, Chicago. All of these cultures were identified physiologically and culturally as well as morphologically. One culture, isolated from a live oyster, showed mixed flagellation with a normal polar flagellum and one or (more rarely) several lateral flagella of shorter wavelength. This culture was physiologically typical of *Pseudomonas*.

The majority of the plant pathogens, some twenty species, were obtained from Dr. Mortimer P. Starr of the University of California.

The halophilic types (fifteen strains) were mainly from R. A. MacLeod of the Fisheries Research Board of Canada, Vancouver, British Columbia. Aside from being halophilic these organisms were typical *Pseudomonas* species.

25

The ordinary pseudomonads show two types of flagellation, polar monotrichous and polar multitrichous (Fig. 8). Both of these types are quite ubiquitous and often isolated from the human skin, throat, intestines, etc. Both types may produce a greenish pigment but as a rule the monotrichous types produce the most pigment. Pigment production appears to be limited to the carbohydrate oxidizers. The nonoxidizers such as *Pseudomonas diminuta, Pseudomonas stutzeri,* etc. are nonpigmented. The most

---

FIG. 8. The ordinary pseudomonads.

a, b, c. *Pseudomonas aeruginosa.* a. The typical flagellation of a young culture. b. Direct stain of the peritoneal fluid of an infected guinea pig. c. A dividing organism.

d. *P. fluorescens.* Normal polar monotrichous flagellation.

e. *P. diminuta.* Note the extremely short wavelength.

f. *P. nigrifaciens.* This organism is larger than most pseudomonads and the flagellum has an extraordinary long wavelength.

g, h. *Pseudomonas* sp. g. Either a polar monotrichous or a polar multitrichous organism. h. A typical polar multitrichous type.

i. *P. synxantha,* NCIB 8178. Polar multitrichous or lophotrichous flagellation.

j. *P. arsenooxydans,* NCIB 8685. Polar multitrichous flagella with coiling tendency.

k. *Pseudomonas* sp. Polar multitrichous flagella of long wavelength. This culture was received from Dr. S. F. Snieszko as *Aeromonas,* U-21. Its history shows it originally came from R. R. Rucker of the Western Disease Laboratory, Seattle, as No. 28.

l. *P. cuneatus,* comb. nov., ATCC 6972. Typical polar lophotrichous flagellation. This culture is labeled *Vibrio cuneatus* in culture collections. Physiologically and morphologically it is very much like the phytopathogenic pseudomonads.

m. *P. pseudomallei* (*Malleomyces pseudomallei*). Polar multitrichous flagellation. Organism received from Dr. S. Gowan, British Type Culture Collection.

n. *P. chlororaphis,* NCIB 8672. Typical polar monotrichous flagellation.

o. *Pseudomonas* sp., H-163. Short polar monotrichous flagellum. Culture isolated from sputum by Dr. Rudolph Hugh.

p. *P. saccharophila,* ATCC 9114. Typical polar monotrichous flagellation.

q. *P. bookeri,* comb. nov., ATCC 9128. This organism in culture collections is labeled *Alcaligenes bookeri.* It does not attack carbohydrates but the morphology places it in the *Pseudomonas* genus.

r. *P. faecalis* var. *radicans,* comb. nov., ATCC 4741. This organism is labeled *Alcaligenes faecalis* var. *radicans* in culture collections. It does not attack carbohydrates but has the typical flagellation of *Pseudomonas.*

a, c, h. From E. Leifson, *J. Bacteriol.* **62**, 377-389 (1951).

26

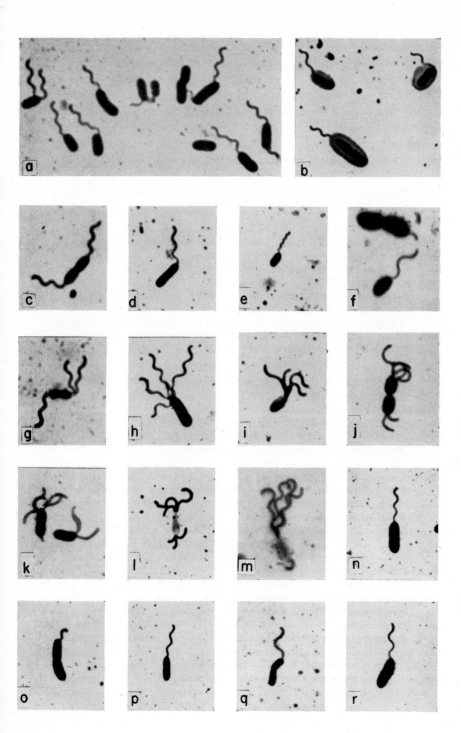

common monotrichous types have a predominantly single flagellum at one or both poles, rarely two flagella at one pole. The flagellar wavelength (Table I) is remarkably uniform averaging from 1.7 to 1.8 microns. The common multitrichous types usually have from two to five flagella at one pole, less often at both poles. The wavelength of these flagella is distinctly greater than that of the monotrichous types, averaging from 2 to 2.5 microns. Flagella of longer wavelengths are rare and usually limited to strains of the plant pathogens. The extremes of wavelengths are illustrated by *P. diminuta,* wavelength 0.7 micron, and *Pseudomonas nigrifaciens,*

Fɪɢ. 9.　s. *Pseudomonas* sp., Fulton 3984. Culture isolated from human pleural fluid at autopsy. Typical polar multitrichous flagellation. The chain of bacilli show where and when the new flagella develop on the daughter cells. In this organism the new flagella develop only after cell division is complete and on the distal pole.

　　t. *Pseudomonas* sp. Organism isolated from the water of the DuPage River. Capsulated organisms of this type are not infrequent in water.

　　u. *Pseudomonas* sp. The organism pictured is an example of mixed flagellation. Note the difference in wavelength of the polar and the lateral flagella. The organism was isolated from a live oyster.

Fɪɢ. 10.　The phytopathogenic pseudomonads.

　　a. *Pseudomonas angulata,* Starr PA 12. Polar multitrichous or lophotrichous flagella.

　　b. *P. cattleyae,* Starr PC 107. Polar multitrichous flagella.

　　c. *P. savastanoi,* Starr PS 111. Polar lophotrichous flagella.

　　d. *P. glycinea,* NCIB 8613. Polar lophotrichous flagella.

　　e, f. *P. washingtoniae,* Starr PW 2. Polar multitrichous flagellation. In e the two upper flagella have distinctly different wavelengths, the shorter measuring 2.02 microns and the longer 2.57 microns. Many individuals in this culture were mototrichous as illustrated in f.

　　g. *Pseudomonas* sp., Starr YCLS. Polar multitrichous flagella. This organism was reported by Dr. Starr to be pectolytic. It was physiologically typical of the genus, and produced a reddish-purple water soluble pigment.

　　h. *P. marginata,* Starr PM 15. Polar multitrichous flagella. The soma is stained rather lightly.

　　i. *P. ribis,* Starr PR 5. Polar multitrichous flagella of unusually long wavelength. Coiled flagella were frequent.

　　j. *Pseudomonas* sp., Smith Cabbage 2B. Polar lophotrichous flagella. This organism was isolated by M. A. Smith, U.S.D.A., from diseased cabbage.

　　k. *P. savastanoi* var. *fraxini,* Starr PS 19. Polar lophotrichous flagellation. The flagella are short with a tendency to coil.

　　l. *P. polycolor,* Starr PP 2. Polar monotrichous flagella. The phytopathogenicity of this organism seems doubtful. Morphologically it is not typical of the phytopathogenic pseudomonads.

28

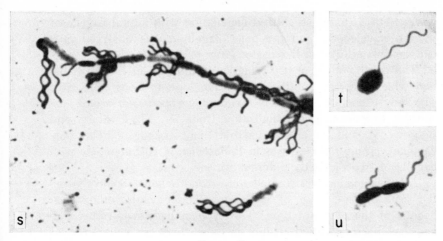

FIGURE 9.

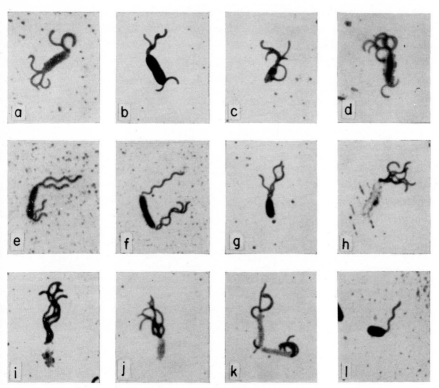

FIGURE 10.

29

wavelength 3.5 microns. Mixed flagellation with lateral flagella of shorter wavelength than the polar flagellum was observed in a culture isolated from a live oyster (Fig. 9).

The plant pathogens are remarkably uniform in their flagellation which is polar multitrichous, often lophotrichous (Fig. 10). The only exception studied is *Pseudomonas polycolor* which, according to personal communication from Dr. M. P. Starr, and Bergey's Manual, is a questionable plant pathogen. The only flagellar variant observed was in *Pseudomonas washingtoniae* with flagella of two distinctly different wavelengths.

All of the halophiles studied were monotrichous. Some showed the typical flagellation of ordinary pseudomonads, others had flagella of the undulant type. This type of flagella is rather rare and has been observed mainly in what may be considered as typical water bacteria, particularly marine. In two of the cultures studied (B-13 and B-28) some individuals had normal flagella, others had undulant flagella. One individual was found with a normal flagellum at one pole and an undulant flagellum at the other pole (Fig. 11a).

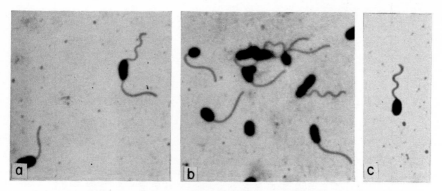

Fig. 11.   The halophilic pseudomonads.

a, b. *Pseudomonas* sp., MacLeod MB-13. The great majority of the individuals in this culture showed polar monotrichous flagella with the undulant shape, and a few with the normal shape. In a is shown an individual, probably about to divide, with a normal flagellum at the upper pole and an undulant flagellum at the lower pole. The undulant flagellar type was seen in several strains of halophilic pseudomonads.

c. *Pseudomonas* sp., MacLeod B-28. Polar monotrichous flagellation of normal type.

TABLE I
MEAN FLAGELLAR WAVELENGTHS OF *Pseudomonas* SPECIES

Species	Strain	Wave-length (microns)	Species	Strain	Wave-length (microns)	Species	Strain	Wave-length (microns)
P. aeruginosa Glucose positive, lactose negative, nitrate reduced to nitrogen gas	H-1	1.67	*Pseudomonas* sp. Monotrichous, glucose negative	H-21	1.96	*P. diminuta*		0.65
	H-55	1.81		H-22	2.18	*P. saccharophila*	ATCC 9114	1.80
	H-58	1.76		H-25	1.48	*P. chlororaphis*	NCIB 8672	1.95
	H-59	1.86		H-26	1.76	*P. bookeri*	ATCC 9128	1.96
	H-66	1.82		H-28	1.88	*P. faecalis* var. *radicans*	ATCC 4741	2.18
	H-111	1.69		H-38	1.87	*P. synxantha*	NCIB 8178	2.33
	H-112	1.87		H-125	1.50	*P. pseudomallei*	Gowan	2.40
	H-113	1.69		H-205	1.76	*P. cuneatus*	ATCC 6972	2.77
	H-122	1.78		H-231	1.71	*P. nigrifaciens*	NCIB 8614	3.07
	H-141	1.68		Group mean	1.79	Plant pathogens		
	H-144	1.67	*Pseudomonas* sp. Monotrichous, lactose positive	H-155	1.88	*P. polycolor*	PP2	1.66
				H-284	1.43	*P. glycinea*	NCIB 8613	1.86
				H-295	1.55	*P. cattleyae*	PC107	2.32
				H-296	1.52	*P. marginata*	PM15	2.41
				H-307	1.58	*P. washingtoniae*	PW2	{2.02, 2.57}
				H-308	1.60	*P. savastanoi* var. *fraxini*	PS19	2.60
				H-309	1.55	*P. angulata*	PA12	2.70
				H-310	1.60	*P. lachrymans*	PL3	2.70
				H-311	1.55			
				H-312	1.54			
				Group mean	1.58			

TABLE I (*continued*)

Species	Strain	Wave-length (microns)
	H-208	1.62
	H-209	1.72
Species mean		1.72
P. fluorescens and allied species; glucose positive, lactose negative, nitrate reduced to nitrite	H-2	1.59
	H-7	1.72
	H-129	1.86
	H-155	1.88
	H-163	2.03
	H-198	1.76
	H-203	1.79
	H-205	1.76
Group mean		1.80

Species	Strain	Wave-length (microns)
Pseudomonas sp. Multitrichous	H-27	2.54
	H-153	3.00
	H-154	2.15
	H-162	2.25
	H-193	2.32
	H-197	2.40
	H-200	2.34
	H-213	2.12
	H-229	2.06
	H-248	2.78
	H-257	2.33
	H-430	2.34
Group mean		2.38

Species	Strain	Wave-length (microns)
P. alliicola	PA8	2.79
P. cichorii	PC26	2.88
P. ribis	PR3	3.36
Halophiles		
Pseudomonas sp.	B-13	{ 1.50 / 4.0
Pseudomonas sp.	B-28	2.0

33

10. *Methanomonas*

One culture labeled *Pseudomonas methanica* was received from J. W. Foster of the University of Texas (Fig. 12). The organisms were stained directly from the original slant. Subcultures on peptone media did not grow. The organism was fairly well flagellated with a single polar flagellum of normal curvature. No variants were observed. The average flagellar wavelength was 1.77 microns with an average amplitude of 0.51 micron.

11. *Protaminobacter*

One strain each of *Protaminobacter ruber* (NRRL,B-1048) and *Protaminobacter alboflavus* (NRRL,B-1051) were received from Dr. W. B. Haynes of the Northern Regional Research Laboratory (NRRL), U.S.D.A., Peoria, Illinois. The culture of *P. ruber* produced reddish colonies on agar, did not acidify any carbohydrate media tested, and was motile (Fig. 13). *P. alboflavus* produced a deep yellow pigment on agar, showed no effect on any carbohydrate tested, and was nonmotile. Both cultures appeared to be typical.

Flagellar Characteristics

P. alboflavus was atrichous. *P. ruber* in moist preparation showed a few individuals with rapid linear motion characteristic of polar monotrichous bacteria. Flagella stain showed a few individuals with a single polar flagellum. The bacterial soma did not take the flagella stain to any extent and counterstain was used. The flagellar curvature was uniform, with an average wavelength of 2.01 microns and average amplitude of 0.54 micron. Flagellar variations were not observed.

Fig. 12. a. *Methanomonas methanica* (*Pseudomonas methanica*). Polar monotrichous flagellation.

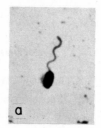

Fig. 13. a. *Protaminobacter ruber*, NRRL, B-1048. Typical organism showing polar monotrichous flagellation. With most individuals on the slide the soma did not take the flagella stain, unlike the one photographed.

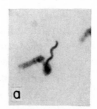

12. *Xanthomonas*

The genus *Xanthomonas* is quite well defined. Typical species are characterized by their polar monotrichous flagellation, the yellow water-insoluble pigmentation, and rather feeble oxidative metabolism of glucose and some other carbohydrates. Nonflagellated strains are common. The phytopathogenic types are best known, but nonpathogenic types also exist.

CULTURES

Thirty-nine cultures were studied of which thirty-eight were phytopathogenic types received from Dr. M. P. Starr of the University of California. Of these thirty-eight cultures twenty-one were typical with polar monotrichous flagellation. The rest were either nonflagellated (seventeen strains) or atypical in other respects. Only one nonpathogenic culture was studied, namely, *Xanthomonas arsenooxydans,* received from the National Collection of Industrial Bacteria (NCIB) as 8688.

FIG. 14. a. *Xanthomonas campestris*, XC-16. Polar monotrichous flagella.

b. *X. campestris*, XC-16. This picture is included to show the very rare occurrence in *Xanthomonas* of two flagella at the same pole.

c. *X. amaranthicola*, XA-120R. Polar monotrichous flagella.

d. *X. amaranthicola*, XA-120R. This picture may be interpreted in two ways, either as representing one organism with two different polar flagella, or as two organisms, each with a different polar flagellum. The wavelength of the shorter flagellum is exactly one half that of the longer flagellum.

e. *X. papavericola*, XP-161. Polar monotrichous flagella.

f. *X. manihotis*, XM-12. Rather long polar flagellum but otherwise typical.

g. *X. vignicola*, XV-118. Long polar flagellum with irregular wavelengths and amplitudes. This was common in some strains.

h. *X. ricinicola*, XR-101. Typical polar flagellum.

i. *X. rubrilineans*, XR-2. Polar monotrichous flagellation.

j. *X. zinniae*, XZ-101. Typical polar flagellum.

k. *X. zinniae*, XZ-101. This illustrates a variant with a flagellum of longer than average wavelength.

l. *X. tardicrescens*, ST-1. The average wavelength of this species is significantly shorter than that of the more typical *Xanthomonas* species.

m. *X. arsenooxydans*, NCIB 8688. Polar monotrichous flagella. Note the rather long wavelength and coiling tendency of the flagella.

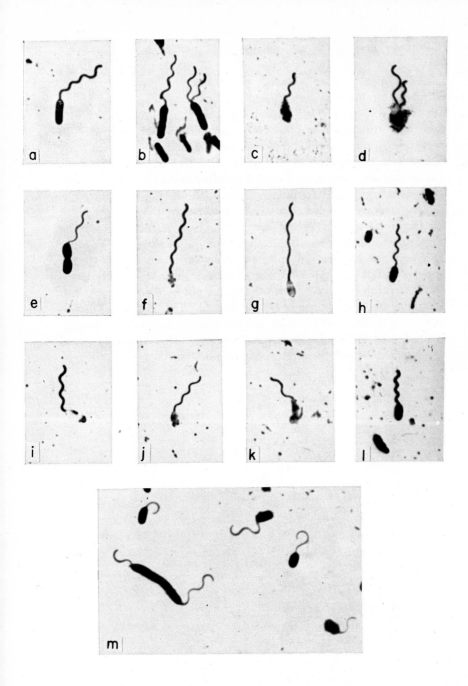

37

All typical strains showed polar monotrichous flagellation. Atrichous strains are common and the strains which are flagellated are often very poorly so. In some species the flagella are of uniform curvature while in others the curvature is very irregular. In two species were found individuals with flagella of two distinctly different wavelengths (Figs. 14d, j, k). The one culture of *X. arsenooxydans* studied was well flagellated with flagella of rather long wavelength and frequently coiled (Table II).

One culture labeled *Bacterium tardicrescens* was typical of *Xanthomonas* species except for failure to oxidize glucose. The flagellar wavelength was significantly less than that of all the other *Xanthomonas* species. In spite of these variations this organism appears sufficiently typical to be classified as *Xanthomonas tardicrescens* comb. nov. *X. rubrilineans* did not oxidize glucose, was nonpigmented but morphologically typical. The strain of *Xanthomonas beticola* studied was peritrichously flagellated, nonpigmented, and oxidized glucose and sucrose. This organism could be classified in the genus *Agrobacterium*.

TABLE II

MEAN FLAGELLAR WAVELENGTHS OF *Xanthomonas* SPECIES

Species	Strain	Wavelength (microns)	Species	Strain	Wavelength (microns)
X. amaranthicola	XA120R	1.83 (3.6)[a]	X. pruni	XP 110	1.84
X. begoniae	XB 10	1.91	X. ricinicola	XR 101	1.75
X. campestris	XC 3	1.78	X. rubrilineans	XR 2	1.79
X. campestris	XC 16	1.65	X. taraxaci	X(D-1)	1.80
X. geranii	XG 1	1.78	X. vasculorum	XV 101	1.77
X. hederae	XH 106	1.83	X. vesicatoria	XV 23	1.80
X. hyacinthi	XH 8	1.74	X. vignicola	XV 117	1.82
X. juglandis	XJ 120	1.85	X. vignicola	XV 118	1.90 (2.9)[a]
X. malvacearum	XM 106	1.77	X. zinniae	XZ 101	1.81
X. manihotis	XM 12	1.77	X. tardicrescens	ST 1	1.50
X. papavericola	XP 5	1.81 (2.6–3.4)[a]	X. translucens	XT4	2.10
X. papavericola	XP 161	1.86			
X. pelargonii	XP 8	1.79		Genus mean	1.79
X. pelargonii	XP 30	1.75			

[a] Figures in parentheses are wavelengths of variants.

39

13. *Mycoplana*

A culture of each of the two species of *Mycoplana, Mycoplana dimorpha* and *Mycoplana bullata* (Fig. 15) were received from Dr. William B. Haynes of the Northern Regional Research Laboratory in Peoria, Illinois. The history of these cultures show that they were received by the Peoria Laboratory directly from Dr. Thornton and presumably are authentic. Physiologically both cultures showed some differences from the original description as recorded in the Bergey Manual. Neither strain reduced nitrate to either nitrite or nitrogen gas. Both strains oxidized glucose, *dimorpha* with slight acidity and *bullata* with considerable acidity.

FLAGELLAR CHARACTERISTICS

M. dimorpha was rather poorly flagellated with most often one flagellum per organism, fairly often two flagella, and occasionally three or four flagella per organism. The flagellar arrangement was peritrichous. No flagellar variants were seen. The average wavelength was 1.57 microns with amplitude of 0.56 micron. *M. bullata* was very motile and well flagellated with polar monotrichous flagella. Only one type of flagella was seen. The flagellar wavelength was very short averaging only 0.91 micron.

TOXONOMIC COMMENTS

The writer cannot see much, if any, justification for the continued existence of the genus *Mycoplana*. *M. bullata* fits very well into the genus *Pseudomonas*. Its somewhat unusual flagellar curvature and, perhaps, physiology would justify retention of the specific epithet and the organism could well be named *Pseudomonas bullata* comb. nov. *M. dimorpha* could well fit into the genus *Achromobacter*. As a matter of fact the characteristics given for *Achromobacter cycloclastes* in Bergey's Manual agree more closely with the characteristics of the strain of *M. dimorpha* studied than with the characteristics given for *M. dimorpha*. The suggestion is made that *M. dimorpha* be considered a synonym of *Achromobacter cycloclastes* and that the genus *Mycoplana* be dropped.

40

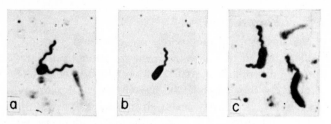

Fig. 15. a. *Mycoplana dimorpha* (*Achromobacter cycloclastes*), NRRL B-1091. Flagella with peritrichous arrangement and normal shape.

b, c. *M. bullata* (*Pseudomonas bullata*), NRRL B-1090. Polar monotrichous flagellation. Flagellar wavelength exceptionally short.

41

14. *Lophomonas*

In the genus *Lophomonas* are classified a group of ubiquitous bacteria found in soil, water, and occasionally isolated from human and animal material such as feces, blood, etc. They are characterized by their distinctive flagellation and failure to metabolize carbohydrates. Thirty-seven strains have been studied in the author's laboratory. All were sufficiently alike to be placed in a single species, *Lophomonas faecalis* (Fig. 16).

FLAGELLAR CHARACTERISTICS

All strains of *Lophomonas* by definition are polar multitrichous or lophotrichous. The flagella tend to be relatively short with very long wavelength such that it is rare to find a flagellum with a complete wave. This type of flagellation is also typical of spirilla but rare in other bacteria.

Several years ago a culture was received from the American Type Culture Collection labeled *Vibrio percolans*, 8461. When this culture was stained both polar and peritrichous individuals were observed on the slides. Some individuals showed both polar and lateral flagella of different wavelength. By plating, the original culture could be separated into pure variants with polar and peritrichous flagella, respectively. The mixed type could not be isolated and is an unstable transitional type. The two flagellar variants were physiologically identical but differed slightly in flagellar antigenicity. The polar variant continued to produce peritrichous forms but the peritrichous variant appears to be stable. In other words, the mutation is always from the polar type to the peritrichous type and never the reverse. This type of mutation appears to be the first of its kind ever described and substantiated by photomicrographs of the mutants and their intermediates. The mutation raises a serious problem in bacterial taxonomy and suggests that a closer relationship exists between polar and nonpolar flagellates than our present taxonomy indicates. The peritrichous mutant is a typical *Alcaligenes* sp. with curly flagella. None of the other thirty-six strains of *Lophomonas* studied have shown any evidence of a similar, or any, morphological mutation.

The wavelength of the polar flagella is somewhat indefinite since a complete wave is rarely found and only half waves can be measured. The wavelengths and amplitudes of the polar flagella of the various strains studied did not show significant differences. The mean wavelength of the polar flagella for the species was

42

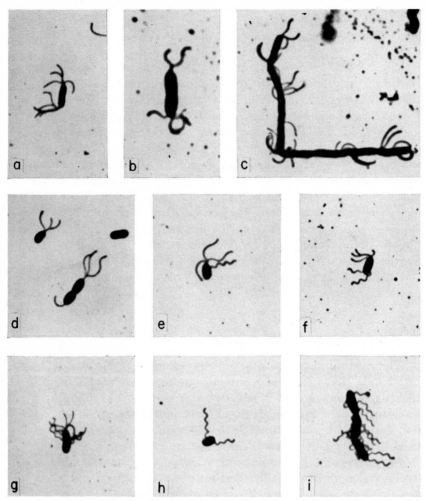

FIG. 16. a, b, c. *Lophomonas faecalis.* Typical polar lophotrichous flagellation. In c is shown the filamentous form.

d, e, f, g, h, i. *L. faecalis* (*Vibrio percolans*), ATCC 8461. In d is shown the polar lophotrichous type which mutates through intermediates e, f, and g to the peritrichous flagellated types h and i. Note the difference in wavelength of the polar and the lateral flagella.

b. From E. Leifson, *J. Bacteriol.* **62**, 377-389 (1951). d, f. From E. Leifson, and R. Hugh, *J. Bacteriol.* **65**, 263-271 (1953). a, c, e. From T. P. Galarneault, and E. Leifson, *Can. J. Microbiol.* **2**, 102-110 (1956).

3.10 microns and the amplitude 1.08 microns. The mean wavelength of the peritrichous mutant was 1.05 microns with amplitude of 0.42 micron. The wavelength of the polar flagella is thus almost exactly three times that of the lateral flagella.

15. *Acetomonas*

The bacteria which are used for the commercial production of vinegar may be classified into two groups which are distinctly different both physiologically and morphologically. For these groups the generic names *Acetomonas* and *Acetobacter* have been suggested. In the genus *Acetobacter* are placed the organisms which oxidize acetic acid (and some other acids) to carbon dioxide and water, and have peritrichous flagella, if any. In the genus *Acetomonas* are placed the organisms which do not oxidize acetic acid and which have polar flagella, if any (Fig. 17).

Ten cultures representing the various named species of *Acetomonas* were studied. Five of these were received from Prof. Frateur of Louvain University in Belgium, and five from W. B. Haynes of the U.S.D.A. in Peoria, Illinois. All were physiologically and culturally typical of the genus. Nine of the cultures were motile and one was nonmotile.

FLAGELLAR CHARACTERISTICS

The motility and flagellation of *Acetomonas* is generally much better than that of *Acetobacter*. All strains showed polar multitrichous flagellation with flagella of uniform shape and quite short wavelength. The number of flagella per individual varied among the strains with some strains showing many monotrichous individuals, others only a few. The flagellar wavelengths of all the strains averaged 1.4 microns with a range of 1.2 to 1.5 microns. This wavelength is unusually short for polar multitrichous bacteria and strikingly different from the polar multitrichous pseudomonads.

44

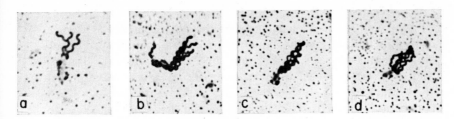

Fig. 17. a. *Acetomonas suboxydans* var. *roseum*, F-16. Polar multi-trichous flagellation. The soma below the flagella is stained rather faintly.

b. *A. suboxydans*, B-72. Two organisms, one with a tuft of five typical polar flagella and the other with a single short flagellum.

c. *A. melanogena*, F-8. A typical tuft of polar flagella extending up from the faintly stained soma.

d. *A. melanogena*, B-58. A typical tuft of five polar flagella with a more faintly stained soma.

a, b, c, d. From E. Leifson, *Antonie van Leeuwenhoek, J. Microbiol. Serol.* **20**, 102-110 (1954).

16. *Acetobacter*

Nine cultures of *Acetobacter* were received from W. B. Haynes of the U.S.D.A. in Peoria, Illinois; nine cultures from Prof. Frateur of Louvain University in Belgium; one culture from C. B. van Niel, University of California; one culture from ATCC; and one culture from J. L. Shimwell, British Vinegars Ltd. Of these twenty-one cultures, six were motile and flagellated. All were typical of the genus.

FLAGELLAR CHARACTERISTICS

Acetobacter strains are often nonmotile and those which show motility are usually poorly flagellated even under the most favorable growth conditions. A fairly satisfactory medium is glucose-peptone-yeast extract broth at pH 6, incubated at 20° C. On centrifugation the organisms tend to clump and few individual bacteria are likely to be found on the slides. The flagella, however, stain readily.

The six motile cultures in the collection showed peritrichous flagellation. The shape of the flagella varied considerably among the different strains. In some the flagella were mainly of the coiled type with long but very irregular wavelength of 3–4 microns. In other cultures the flagella were more uniform in shape with wavelengths for example of 2.36 microns for *Acetobacter aceti*, F-4; 2.21 microns for *Acetobacter orleanense*, B-55; and 1.82 microns for *Acetobacter aceti*, Shimwell. The Shimwell culture was somewhat different from the others in being much better flagellated, showed less clumping, and having flagella of shorter wavelength and smaller amplitude than the others (Fig. 18).

17. *Zymomonas*

Through the courtesy of J. L. Shimwell one culture of *Zymomonas* (*Saccharomonas*) *anaerobia* was received from Bristol University in England. A culture of *Pseudomonas* (*Zymomonas*) *lindneri* obtained from Dr. Haynes was nonflagellated. Another species of this genus, *Zymomonas mobile,* was not obtained. These bacteria are often referred to in industry as cider sickness organisms.

FLAGELLAR CHARACTERISTICS

The one culture of *Zymomonas anaerobia* from Bristol University showed organisms with a tuft of polar flagella of wavelength averaging 2.5 microns (Fig. 19). No variants were observed.

46

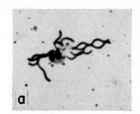 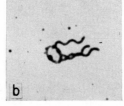 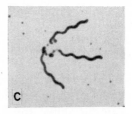

FIG. 18.   a. *Acetobacter rancens,* F-5. A clump of two organisms with lightly stained soma. Peritrichous flagella of normal curvature.

b. *A. aceti,* B-1036. A single individual, rarely found on slides of this genus, showing peritrichous flagellation. The flagellar curvature is normal.

c. *A. aceti,* Shimwell. This strain was better flagellated than the other strains studied and the organisms showed less tendency to clump. Many individuals showed from five to seven flagella. The flagellar arrangement is typically peritrichous.

a, b. From E. Leifson, *Antonie van Leeuwenhoek, J. Microbiol. Serol.* **20,** 102-110 (1954).

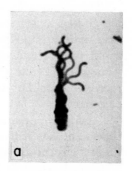

FIG. 19. a. *Zymomonas anaerobia* var. *pomaceae.* The picture shows the typical flagellation of this organism. The soma of the organism shown is somewhat larger than the average.

18. *Aeromonas*

The genus *Aeromonas* has fairly recently been created for a group of organisms formerly classified as *Pseudomonas*. These organisms differ from the type species of *Pseudomonas*, *Pseudomonas aeruginosa*, by their fermentative metabolism of carbohydrates, absence of pigmentation, and a tendency to produce lateral flagella in addition to the polar flagellum in young cultures. In this group are found bacteria which are pathogenic for frogs (*Pseudomonas hydrophila*, *Proteus hydrophila*, etc.), for fish, and other cold blooded animals.

CULTURES

Ten cultures have been studied. Six of these were isolated in the United States and supplied by Dr. S. F. Snieszko of the U.S. Fish and Wildlife Service. They were isolated mainly from diseased fish. Three of the cultures originated from Holland and were isolated from water. One culture, *Aeromonas formicans*, was received from Dr. H. Pivnich, University of Nebraska. All the cultures were physiologically typical of the genus. One culture was peritrichously flagellated (Kluyver strain L-418) when received and has remained unchanged over a period of several years. From personal communication this culture apparently was polar flagellated when first isolated. It has the typical physiology of *Aeromonas* and appears to be a stable variant (?). The coiled shape of the flagella is also found in the polar flagella of other strains as may be observed from the illustrations.

FLAGELLAR CHARACTERISTICS

In cultures which were incubated past the logarithmic phase of growth, i.e. overnight at temperatures between 20° and 37° C., all strains of *Aeromonas* studied showed mainly polar monotrichous flagellation. Some strains produced only the normal type of polar flagellum while in the other strains several types of polar flagella were produced: undulant, normal, and coiled. The undulant type has a wavelength averaging 3.5 microns and the normal type a

48

wavelength averaging 1.7 microns. The ratio of the two wavelengths is thus almost exactly 2:1. By plating in semisolid agar, colonies showing much and little spreading were found. When these were fished the small spreading colonies showed bacteria mainly with the undulant type of polar flagellum while the bacteria from the larger spreaders had mainly the normal type of polar flagellum. However the cultures from the fished colonies were not pure for one or the other type of flagella, and variation from the one type to the other must take place at a high rate. Individuals with both types of flagella are occasionally seen, even at the same pole, as illustrated in Fig. 20d. The undulant flagellum is apparently less efficient for locomotion than the normal flagellum. Individuals with coiled polar flagella were occasionally observed. In one strain (Kluyver L-417) the coiled flagella were very common and often multiple as illustrated in Figs. 20h and i. The peritrichous variant with coiled flagella may have originated from this type with multiple coiled polar flagella. However, a mutation from polar to peritrichous was not observed in the author's laboratory.

The most unique feature of *Aeromonas* flagellation is the formation of lateral flagella in very young cultures. This phenomenon, to a variable extent, has been observed in all but one of the strains studied. In one strain (Kluyver L-417) the lateral flagella had the same wavelength as the polar flagellum. With the other strains the lateral flagella had a definitely shorter wavelength than the polar flagellum. In all the strains studied the lateral flagella showed the same wavelength of 1.5 microns irrespective of the wavelength of the polar flagellum. Individuals with undulant, normal, or coiled polar flagella produced normal lateral flagella of the same wavelength. Coiled or undulant lateral flagella were never observed in the young cultures.

49

Fɪɢ. 20.   a, b, c, d, e, f.   *Aeromonas* sp., Snieszko U-6. This typical culture of *Aeromonas* was isolated from diseased fish. Old cultures showed a mixture of polar flagellated individuals, some with the normal type of flagella and some with the undulant type, as illustrated in a and b. One individual was found with a normal and an undulant flagellum at the same pole (d). In young cultures lateral flagella were found, both on individuals with a normal polar flagellum and with an undulant polar flagellum, as illustrated in e and f. Note the similarity of the lateral flagella in the two types.

g, h, i, j. *Aeromonas hydrophila*, ATCC 7965. In old cultures were found individuals with a normal single polar flagellum, illustrated in g, and individuals with a polar tuft of coiled flagella, illustrated in h. In young cultures individuals with lateral flagella of short wavelength were found as illustrated in i and j.

k, l. *A. liquefaciens*, Kluyver L-417. Old cultures of this strain showed normal single polar flagella only, while young cultures showed many individuals with peritrichous flagellation. In this strain the polar and lateral flagella were of the same wavelength.

m. *A. formicans*, Pivnick. Normal polar monotrichous flagellation. Both old and young cultures showed only this type of flagellation. This organism may not be a pathogen for cold blooded animals.

n. *Aeromonas* sp., Snieszko, U-23. The polar flagellum illustrated is unusual in that the wavelength gets progressively longer from the soma out. This type of flagellum was seen frequently in several strains of *Aeromonas* but is very rare in other bacterial genera.

o. *Aeromonas* (?) sp. This culture was received as *A. liquefaciens*, Kluyver L-418. It is physiologically typical of *Aeromonas* and may be a morphological mutant but definite evidence to this effect is lacking. All individuals in the culture showed the coiled peritrichous flagellation. Morphologically and physiologically this organism is very similar to a nonpigmented *Serratia*.

g, h, i, j, k, l, o.   From E. Leifson, and R. Hugh, *J. Bacteriol.* **65**, 263-271 (1953).

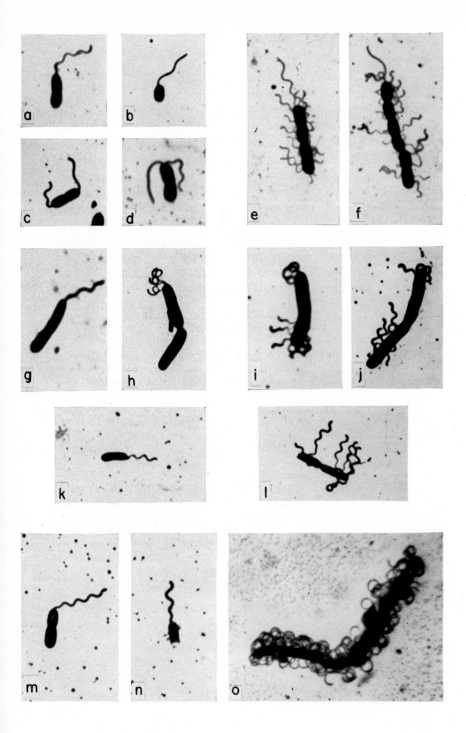

19. *Vibrio*

The genus *Vibrio* is composed of bacteria which typically have a slight somatic curvature and a single polar flagellum (Fig. 21). The somatic curvature is an unreliable characteristic which has, perhaps, little taxonomic significance. Carbohydrates are fermented with acid production but no gas. Most strains are very proteolytic, actively liquefying gelatin and coagulated serum. Bergey's Manual, 6th ed., recognizes twenty-two species. Several of these species are definitely out of place in the genus, such as *Vibrio percolans* (*Lophomonas*) and *Vibrio cuneatus* (*Pseudomonas*). Several other species obtained from culture collections had peritrichous flagella and therefore are not *Vibrio* species. These latter, of course, may have been contaminants which had replaced the original vibrios. In this category may, perhaps, be *Vibrio jejuni*, ATCC 11734, which had peritrichous flagella.

Fig. 21. a. *Vibrio cholerae*, Freter 144. Typical specimen showing polar monotrichous flagellation.

b. *V. proteus*. This picture is of an old stock strain labeled *V. finklor-prior*.

c. *Vibrio* (*Pseudomonas*) *rubicundus*, Haynes B-782. This organism is more properly classified as *Pseudomonas* sp. since it did not attack carbohydrates.

d. *V. tyrogenus*, Haynes B-1033. The soma of this organism often resembled a spirillum with several curves. A very few individuals had multiple flagella at one pole.

e, f. *Vibrio* sp., MacLeod MB-26. This is a halophilic vibrio from the Pacific Ocean. The organisms with the straight soma were more numerous than those with a curved soma.

g, h. *V. fetus*, Hansen. Most of the individuals in the culture studied showed polar monotrichous flagellation illustrated in g. A fair number showed polar multitrichous flagellation illustrated in h. The resemblance to spirilla is striking.

i, j. *V. fetus*, Ryff 28099. In i is shown an organism with several curves like a spirillum. In j is shown the rounded types or "microcysts" so typical of spirilla.

k, l. *V. coli*, Di Liello 505. The organism illustrated in l is in the process of microcyst formation.

m. *V. coli*, Di Liello 498. The bipolar flagellation was common in the *V. coli* cultures as it was in the *V. fetus* cultures.

n. *Vibrio* (?) *jejuni*, ATCC 11734. This is obviously not a *Vibrio* sp. In the culture studied the soma was generally curved as illustrated. The peritrichous flagellation is unmistakable. Cultures other than this could not be obtained.

52

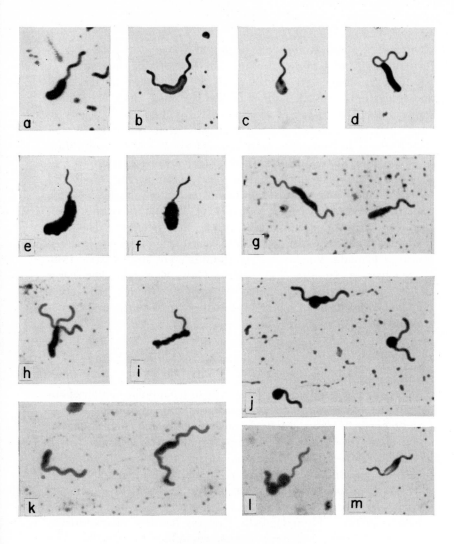

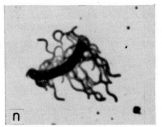

53

Included in the study were several strains of *V. cholerae* from the University of Chicago through Dr. Rolf Freter; one strain of *Vibrio fetus* from P. Arne Hansen of the University of Maryland and four strains from J. F. Ryff of the Wyoming State Veterinary Laboratory; two strains of *Vibrio coli* from Leo R. Di Liello in Maryland; one strain of *Vibrio tyrogenus* from W. B. Haynes of the Northern Regional Research Laboratory, U.S.D.A.; and *Vibrio proteus* from stock. *Vibrio rubicundus,* received from W. B. Haynes, was a polar monotrichous fairly straight rod which did not ferment glucose and, if authentic, is better classified in the genus *Pseudomonas.* Several strains of halophilic vibrios, both luminescent and nonluminescent types, were studied. The non-luminescent strains came from R. A. MacLeod, Fisheries Research Board of Canada, Vancouver. The luminescent strains came from R. Spencer of Humber Laboratory, Hull, England. The latter strains are discussed under *Photobacterium* although the author does not wholeheartedly favor the existence of the genus *Photobacterium.*

FLAGELLAR CHARACTERISTICS

All typical flagellated vibrios appear to have polar monotrichous flagellation. Multiple flagella at one pole and bipolar flagella are rare except in *V. fetus.* Multiple polar flagella and bipolar flagella are common in *V. fetus.* The soma of the latter organism often has several curves like a spirillum. In some cultures the rounded forms (microcysts) were numerous, which is also characteristic of spirilla. The polar flagella, when multiple, frequently are short with few curves of large amplitude, which gives a rather typical spirillum picture. Physiologically *V. fetus* has few characteristics of a typical vibrio and more closely resembles the spirilla. The original classification of this organism as a *Spirillum* has much in its favor. Morphologically the two cultures of *V. coli* resembled those of *V. fetus* rather closely. Microcysts were also observed in *V. coli* but not multiple polar flagella.

Morphologically the halophilic vibrios do not differ significantly from the nonhalophilic types. In artificial culture the soma is usually a short or oval rod, rarely curved. Identification as vibrios is based on the polar monotrichous flagellation, the fermentative

54

action on carbohydrates, and other physiological characteristics. All strains studied liquefied gelatin. In most instances the flagella had normal curvature. The flagellar wavelengths of the species studied are given in Table III.

TABLE III
MEAN FLAGELLAR WAVELENGTHS OF *Vibrio* SPECIES

Species	Strain	Wavelength (microns)
V. cholerae	F-144	2.43
V. proteus	—	2.01
V. fetus	Hansen	2.08
V. fetus	Ryff	1.87
V. tyrogenus	NRRL, B-1033	2.06
V. rubicundus	NRRL, B-782	2.02
V. coli	Di Liello	1.85
Vibrio sp. (halophilic)	MacLeod	1.95

20. *Desulfovibrio*

The several species of *Desulfovibrio* listed in Bergey's Manual, 6th ed., are stated to be morphologically indistinguishable. A culture was received from Dr. C. E. ZoBell of the Scripps Oceanographic Institute in La Jolla, California. According to Dr. ZoBell the culture was not pure and this was verified by staining. The organism pictured was most typical for a vibrio and it is reproduced with this questionable identification (Fig. 22).

FLAGELLAR CHARACTERISTICS

Assuming the organism referred to above to be a *Desulfovibrio* species, the flagellation is polar monotrichous. The flagellar wavelength is quite long, averaging 3.0 microns. Since a pure culture was not available for study, nothing can be said about variations.

21. *Cellvibrio*

Bergey's Manual, 6th ed., lists four species of *Cellvibrio* which are differentiated on the bases of growth on glucose and starch agar and degree of pigmentation. Several cultures were obtained for study. One culture was obtained from W. B. Haynes of the Northern Regional Research Laboratory, U.S.D.A., Peoria, Illinois. This culture (B-668) was simply labeled *Cellvibrio* sp. Four cultures were obtained from Dr. H. W. Reuszer of Purdue University. Two were labeled *Cellvibrio vulgaris*, strain 6, and strain 122. Two were labeled *Cellvibrio fulvus*, strain 18, and strain 102. All five of these cultures grew well on glucose agar slants, producing at first a yellow water-insoluble pigment which later turned brown. In glucose-yeast extract broth growth was fair with the formation of a brown pellicle. In dextrose semisolid agar all cultures produced a very slight acidity under aerobic conditions but no acidity under anaerobic conditions. Physiologically and culturally the five cultures appeared to be more or less identical.

FLAGELLAR CHARACTERISTICS

All four of the Reuszer strains showed the same two types of flagellation, differing only in the relative proportions of the two types. *C. fulvus*, Reuszer strain 18, showed mainly small curved rods with single polar flagella of relatively long wavelength as illustrated in Fig. 23b. Also present in lesser numbers was a small straight rod with a single polar flagellum of relatively short wave-

56

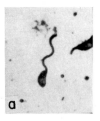

FIG. 22. a. *Desulfovibrio* sp. (?), ZoBell strain 249. Typical polar monotrichous flagellation with long wavelength and large amplitude.

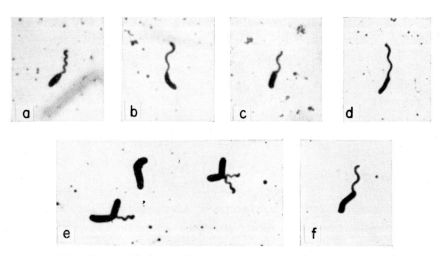

FIG. 23. a. *Cellvibrio vulgaris*, Reuszer 122. The soma is straight with rounded ends and with a single polar flagellum of relatively short wavelength.

b. *C. fulvus*, Reuszer 18. The soma is typically vibrio shaped with a single polar flagellum of relatively long wavelength.

c. *Cellvibrio* sp., Haynes B-668. Single polar flagellum with the long wavelength. In this individual the soma is only very slightly curved.

d. *C. vulgaris*, Reuszer 122. Polar monotrichous flagella with the longer wavelength.

e. *C. fulvus*, Reuszer 102. This shows the same type of organism illustrated in a. In addition to the individuals with the single polar flagellum the rather unusual situation pictured was quite common. With most bacteria in which the new flagella develop before cell division is completed, bipolar or amphitrichous flagellation is produced. In other words, the distal ends of the daughter cells usually carry the flagella. With the organism pictured it appears as if the region of cell division develops the new flagella.

f. *C. fulvus*, Reuszer 102. Polar monotrichous flagellation of same type shown in b.

57

length as illustrated in Fig. 23a. In *C. fulvus,* Reuszer strain 102, the individuals with the short flagellar wavelength were most abundant but otherwise the two strains were morphologically alike. Both strains of *C. vulgaris* showed the same two types of individuals with the long wavelength type most abundant in Reuszer strain 122. The average flagellar wavelength of the two types was 2.06 microns and 0.84 micron, respectively.

According to letter communication from Dr. Reuszer, he also had observed two somatic types of individuals in his *Cellvibrio* cultures. By plating and fishing single colonies he had not succeeded in obtaining stable pure cultures of each somatic type. The author also plated the cultures and fished a number of typical yellow-brown colonies. The fresh isolates invariably showed only individuals with the short wavelength flagella. Transfers from these isolates showed only individuals with the short wavelength flagella. The long wavelength type was not observed in pure culture and its relationship to the short wavelength type remains undetermined.

22. *Succinovibrio*

One culture of *Succinovibrio dextrinosolvens* C-85 was obtained from Dr. M. Bryant of the U.S.D.A., Beltsville, Maryland (Fig. 24). This culture was isolated from cow rumen fluid. It was strictly anaerobic.

FLAGELLAR CHARACTERISTICS

The one culture studied showed a large rod shaped organism with somatic curvature like a vibrio. A few individuals were flagellated with a single polar flagellum of rather long wavelength, averaging 3.2 microns. No variations were observed.

23. *Lachnospira*

A culture of *Lachnospira multiparus,* D-38, was obtained from Dr. M. Bryant of the U.S.D.A., Beltsville, Maryland (Fig. 25).

FLAGELLAR CHARACTERISTICS

The flagellation of this organism is very unusual. The individual organisms appear as slightly curved rods with a single flagellum originating from the side, usually near the center. This type of flagellation is designated as lateral monotrichous and is quite rare. The one culture studied labeled *Nitrobacter agilis* also seemed to have this type of flagellation. The flagellar wavelength is rather long, averaging 3.0 microns.

58

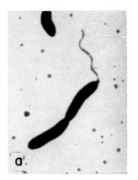

Fig. 24. a. *Succinovibrio dextrinosolvens*, Bryant, C-85. Polar monotrichous flagellation. The flagella stained with some difficulty and rather lightly.

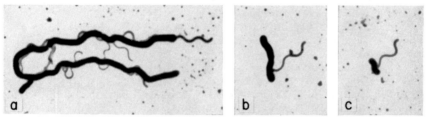

Fig. 25. a. *Lachnospira multiparus*, Bryant D-38. This shows the organism in the filamentous form. The polar location of the flagellum at the end of the filament is not significant since individual organisms did not show polar flagellation.

b, c. *L. multiparus*, Bryant D-38. In c is a single individual showing lateral monotrichous flagellation. In b is shown two individuals, one of which has a single lateral flagellum.

24. Spirillum

A representative collection of twenty-six cultures of *Spirillum* were studied morphologically. One culture of *Spirillum virginianum* was received from C. B. van Niel, Hopkins Marine Station; one culture of *Spirillum serpens* came from the Midwest Culture Service; and all the others from Marion Williams, University of Southern Illinois. The Williams collection of twenty-four cultures was about evenly divided into fresh water and marine forms. The marine forms were cultured in media with

---

Fɪɢ. 26. a. *Spirillum serpens*, Williams. A typical large fresh water spirillum with a tuft of flagella at both ends. Note the relatively short flagella with few curves. Organisms with flagella only at one pole do occur but not as commonly as the amphitrichous types.

b. *Spirillum* sp., Williams LA-1. A fresh water spirillum with a large number of flagella. The tufts of lateral flagella presumably originate at points of somatic cleavage.

c. *Spirillum* sp., Williams Sb-10. A typical, medium sized fresh water spirillum.

d. *S. itersonii*, Giesberger strain. A relatively small fresh water spirillum.

e, f. *S. virginianum*, Hopkins Marine Station 0.1.1. This spirillum tends to be short and only slightly curved. Some individuals may even be perfectly straight like that pictured in e. The flagellation is polar lophotrichous and typical of spirilla.

g. *Spirillum* sp., Williams Sb-9. A typical fresh water spirillum.

h, i, j. *Spirillum* sp., Williams 2E-6. This is a typical marine spirillum. In h is shown the normal or vegetative form, and in i and j, the "microcyst" form. The microcysts are usually slightly oval and may have flagella at one or both poles. The flagella apparently are not disturbed when the vegetative form rounds up or condenses to form the microcyst.

k. *Spirillum* sp. This organism was not isolated in culture but stained directly from the intestinal contents of a dog. The soma is short and twisted into a spiral. The flagellation is polar monotrichous.

l. *S. polymorphum*, Williams. This species was the only one of the twenty-six cultures studied with polar monotrichous flagellation. The culture grew poorly and very slowly on the media used. The organism is rather small and only a few individuals were flagellated. All flagellated individuals had the same type of polar monotrichous flagella.

m. *S. linum*, Williams. This is a typical marine spirillum of average size. The organism to the right shows a flagellum with several curves and relatively short wavelength, along with the more normal flagella of spirilla. This type of flagellum appears to be extremely rare in spirilla and was seen only in this particular culture. It may be considered as equivalent to the curly type of flagella in other bacteria.

e, f. From T. P. Galarneault, and E. Leifson, *Can. J. Microbiol.* **2**, 102-110 (1956). k. From E. Leifson, *J. Bacteriol.* **62**, 377-389 (1951).

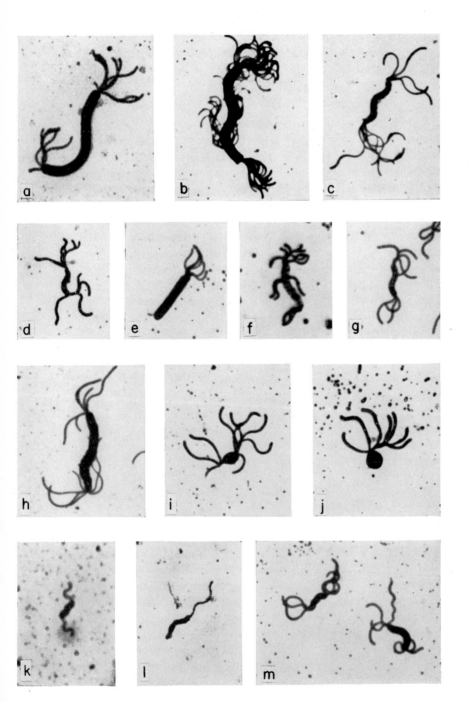

61

3% sodium chloride, the others in ordinary media made with soya peptone. Unfortunately a culture of *Spirillum minus* was not obtained.

All spirilla are polar flagellated, usually polar multitrichous or lophotrichous. Only one named species showed polar monotrichous flagella, namely *Spirillum polymorphum*. A polar monotrichous type was also observed in a smear from the dog intestine and is illustrated in Fig. 26k. The typical flagella of spirilla have a very long wavelength (over 3 microns) and usually less than one complete wave. Only one culture, *Spirillum linum*, showed an occasional flagellum with short wavelength (about 1.5 microns) and several waves (Fig. 26m). This flagellum may be considered as the curly variant although the wavelength is considerably greater than the curly flagella of most bacteria. In the marine forms the oval "microcysts" were much in evidence. These showed the same flagellation as the normal organisms, as illustrated in Figs. 26h, i, j. Although it is usual to find flagella at both ends of a spirillum, organisms with flagella at only one end were present in every culture. In spite of all the statements in the literature about the unusual nature of the flagella on spirilla the author finds them no different fundamentally from the flagella of other bacteria. The genus *Lophomonas* has the same type of flagellation as *Spirillum*, as have also a few *Pseudomonas* types, particularly among the plant pathogens. Most bacteria, however, have flagella with more curves.

25. Azotobacter

Complete agreement on the taxonomy of *Azotobacter* apparently has not been reached. Bergey's Manual lists three species and does not include *Azotobacter vinelandii*. *Azotobacter macrocytogenes* is also not included. Eight strains labeled *Azotobacter chroococcum* were received; one from William D. Haynes of the Northern Regional Research Laboratory of the U.S.D.A., Peoria, Illinois, and seven strains from Perry Wilson of the University of Wisconsin. Four of the Wilson strains showed good motility and were typical in every respect including a light brownish pigmentation. The other strains were nonmotile or so poorly motile as to be unsatisfactory for flagellar studies. Two strains each of *Azotobacter agilis* and *A. vinelandii* were received from Dr. Wilson. The two strains of *A. agilis* showed good motility, while one strain of *A. vinelandii* was motile but the other not. *Azotobacter indicum* 8597 was received from the National Collection of Industrial Bacteria in England and also *A. macrocytogenes* 8700. *A. indicum* 9037, 9038, 9039, and 9540 were received from ATCC. Of the *indicum* strains only ATCC 9038 and 9039 were flagellated. (See Fig. 27.)

Flagellar Characteristics

A. agilis was actively motile and showed good flagellation. The flagella were peritrichously arranged and either normal, coiled, or both coiled and normal on the same individual. *A. vinelandii*, strain Wilson O, was actively motile with peritrichously arranged flagella. Only normal flagella were observed. The four strains of *A. chroococcum* which were motile showed peritrichously arranged flagella. The best stains were obtained from mannitol agar slants without peptone. When the four strains were stained from suspensions made alkaline with dibasic potassium phosphate, prior to the addition of formalin, all showed normal flagella only. However, when stained from suspensions made slightly acid with monobasic potassium phosphate, strains E-2 and E-3 again showed only normal flagella while strains E-7 and E-8 showed curly flagella only. This change of flagellar curvature by change of pH is not common and it is curious to find this difference in strains of *A. chroococcum* which, superficially at least, appear to be alike. *A. indicum*, ATCC strains 9038 and 9039, were slightly motile and some individuals showed peritrichous flagellation. The flagella showed a strong polar tendency, often appearing as a tuft of polar flagella. All the observed flagella of these strains had a short wavelength comparable to the curly type of *A. chroococcum*. Change of pH did not affect the wavelength of these flagella.

A. macrocytogenes, NCIB 8700, showed polar flagellation. The flagella were most frequently single, but occasionally multiple, and this culture must be regarded as polar multitrichous. This organism should, therefore, not be classified in the genus *Azotobacter*. If it is a nonsymbiotic nitrogen fixing organism it could be classified in the genus *Azotomonas*.

63

Fig. 27. a. *Azotobacter chroococcum*, Wilson E-7. Peritrichous flagella with normal curvature. These organisms are from a suspension to which K_2HPO_4 had been added prior to the formalin. The average normal wavelength of this strain was 2.70 microns.

b. *A. chroococcum*, Wilson E-7. Peritrichous flagella with curly curvature. These organisms are from a suspension to which KH_2PO_4 had been added prior to the formalin. The average curly wavelength was 1.20 microns.

c. *A. vinelandii*, Wilson O. Peritrichous flagella of normal curvature. Average normal wavelength was 2.71 microns.

d. *A. agilis,* Wilson 4-4. Peritrichous flagella typical in this culture with partly normal and partly coiled curvature. Average wavelength about 3.2 microns.

e. *A. indicum*, ATCC 9039. Peritrichous flagella of short wavelength comparable to the curly type of *A. chroococcum*. Note the polar tendency of the flagella. The average flagellar wavelength was 1.0 micron.

f, g. *A.* (*Azotomonas*) *macrocytogenes,* NCIB 8700. Polar multitrichous and polar monotrichous flagella. The soma of this organism is much like that of the typical *Azotobacter* strains but the flagella are distinctly different both as to arrangement and shape. Average wavelength was 1.7 microns.

64

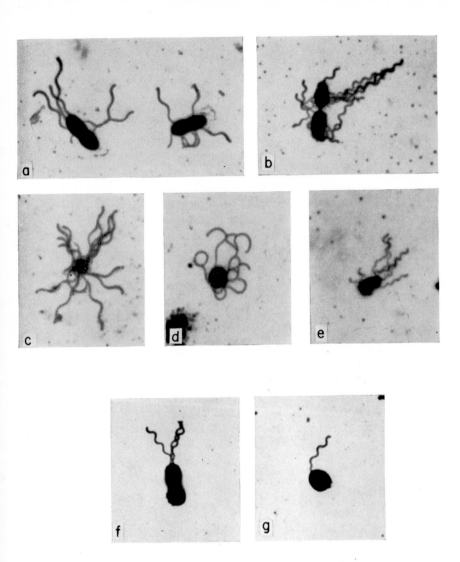

65

26. Azotomonas

The genus *Azotomonas* has only one species, *Azotomonas insolita* (Fig. 28). The organism is described as polar flagellated with one to three flagella, ferments a variety of carbohydrates, including lactose, with acid and gas. In spite of the lactose fermentation "no change" is recorded for milk which seems improbable unless the organism fails to grow in milk. Gas production from carbohydrates by polar flagellated bacteria is so unusual as to cast doubt on the correctness of the description.

One strain of *A. insolita* was obtained from the National Collection of Industrial Bacteria in England. This organism showed peritrichous flagellation. It must be stated, however, that in a somewhat sparsely flagellated organism many individuals will be found with polarly located flagella. This was also the case with the strain of *A. insolita* studied, but lateral flagella were too frequent to cause any doubt that it is peritrichous flagellated. The strain studied was rather poorly flagellated with up to four flagella per individual. The wavelength was rather short, averaging 1.4 microns. If this culture is an authentic *A. insolita* strain then the genus *Azotomonas* must be redefined. Morphologically the organism resembles rather closely some species of *Rhizobium* but does not resemble the common species of *Azotobacter*.

66

Fig. 28. a. *Azotomonas insolita,* NCIB 8627. Peritrichous flagella of rather short wavelength. Many individuals on the slide showed single flagella often at the pole, as well as several flagella at the pole. However, the peritrichous nature of the flagellation seems unquestionable. The flagellation is very similar to some species of *Rhizobium.*

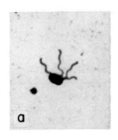

27. *Rhizobium*

The genus *Rhizobium* is composed of a group of bacteria (Fig. 29) which are able to invade the root tissues of specific leguminous plants with the formation of characteristic nodules. The bacteria

Fig. 29. a. From *Vigna sinensis*, 3I6n10. Subpolar monotrichous flagella.

b. From *Phaseolus lunatus*, 3I6d10. Subpolar monotrichous flagellation.

c. From *Phaseolus aureus*, 3I6h7. Subpolar monotrichous flagellation. The organism pictured appears to be made up of three cells with the flagellum originating from the middle of the right end cell.

d. From *Phaseolus angularis*, 3I6f1. Subpolar monotrichous flagellation.

e. From *Phaseolus aconitifolius*, 3I6g1. Subpolar monotrichous flagellation.

f. From *Albizzia julibrissen*, 1Boa2. Subpolar monotrichous flagellation.

g, h, i, j. From *Glycina hispida*, 3I1b59. g. The basic subpolar monotrichous flagellation of this strain. h. A curly flagellum in addition to the normal flagellum. i. Four long curly flagella in addition to the normal flagellum. j. Two curly flagella but no normal flagellum.

k. From *Ulex europaeus*, 3C3a1. Subpolar monotrichous flagellation.

l. From *Lupinus sp.*, 3C2k5. Subpolar monotrichous flagellation.

m, n, o. From *Erythrina indica*, 3I2b1. m. A subpolar flagellum of somewhat peculiar shape. n. Two curly flagella in addition to the normal flagellum which is short and hooked in this strain. o. Two curly flagella only.

p, q. From *Pisum arvense*. Peritrichous flagellation. The peculiar flagella shown in q were common in this strain. Compare it with the illustration of *Agrobacterium rhizogenes*.

r. From *Trifolium dubium*, 3D1x3. Peritrichous flagellation.

s. From *Phaseolus vulgaris*, 3I6c10(a). Peritrichous flagellation.

t. From *Phaseolus vulgaris*, 3I6c14. A curly and a straight flagellum. A most unusual variant.

u. From *Medicago sativa*, 3Doa30. Peritrichous flagellation.

v. From *Melilotus alba*, 3Doh13. Peritrichous flagellation. Note the straight proximal parts of the flagella like those in q above.

w. From *Lotus americanus*, 3Eob1. Peritrichous flagellation.

x. From *Strophostylus pauciflora*, 3I6ml. Peritrichous flagellation.

y. From *Robinia pseudoacacia*, 3F4b7. Peritrichous flagellation.

z. From *Caragana arborescens*, 3F6g2. Peritrichous flagellation.

aa. From *Acacia linifolia*, 1Aoc1. Peritrichous flagellation. This organism shows an unusually large number of flagella for a rhizobium.

bb. From *Wisteria frutescens*, 3F33c1. Peritrichous flagella with strong polar tendency.

cc. From *Lupinus densiflorus*, 3C2n1. Peritrichous flagellation. All three of the strains studied of this origin showed peritrichous flagellation.

dd. From *Phaseolus lunatus*, 3I6d23. Very nice peritrichous flagella. This is one of the two strains from *Phaseolus lunatus* which showed peritrichous flagella. The other nine strains studied showed typical subpolar flagella.

a–d. From E. Leifson, and L. W. Erdman, *Antonie van Leeuwenhoek, J Microbiol. Serol.* **24**, 97-110 (1958).

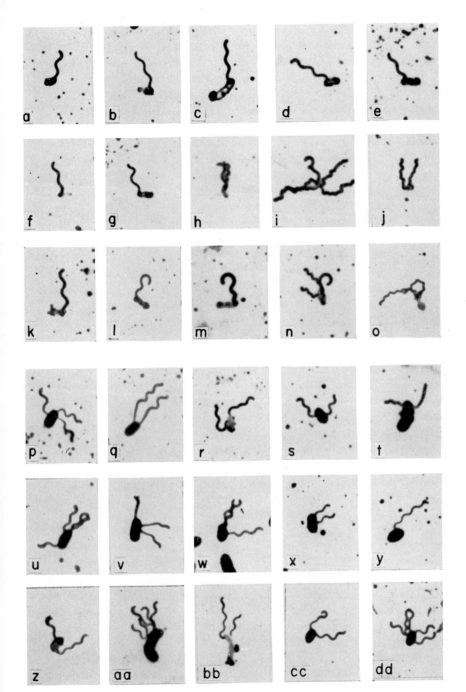

within the nodules fix atmospheric nitrogen and thus furnish nitrates for the growth of the plant. Because of its economic importance the genus has been studied in great detail. Morphologically the genus may be divided into two subgroups, mainly on the basis of flagellation, which correlates fairly well with physiological and cultural characteristics. The "phytopathogenicity" of the organisms is very specific and the genus may be separated into a number of so-called inoculation groups, each group infecting a specific genus or group of genera of legumes. The bacteria in each inoculation group generally have similar morphology and cultural characteristics as shown in Table IV.

The flagellation of eighty-two strains from thirty-seven plant species was studied. All of these were furnished by Dr. L. W. Erdman of the U.S.D.A., Beltsville, Maryland.

Flagellar Characteristics

Most strains of *Rhizobium* are rather poorly flagellated. Various media and cultural conditions were tried to improve the flagellation but with rather limited success. Best results were usually obtained with a peptone-mannitol broth incubated at 20° C. In a few instances an agar medium of same composition gave as good or better results. With a few cultures stains could be made after 1–2 days incubation but most cultures required 3 or more days to produce sufficient growth for staining. The flagella stained readily and none of the cultures were completely devoid of flagellated individuals.

Rhizobium strains show two main types of flagellation, a nonpolar or peritrichous type and a subpolar monotrichous type. The subpolar monotrichous flagellum usually emerges quite close to the somatic pole and at a right angle to the long axis of the soma. This is quite distinct from the situation in polar flagellation where the flagellum emerges in a direction parallel to the long axis of the soma. The subpolar rhizobia are almost invariably monotrichous. Two flagella at the same pole are rarely observed and one flagellum at each pole has never been observed. Of all the strains of rhizobia studied the best flagellation is generally found among the subpolar types.

The other main type of flagellation may be called peritrichous. Most of the strains studied with this type of flagellation were poorly flagellated with most of the flagellated individuals having only one flagellum, rarely several. The flagella, whether single or

70

multiple, showed a tendency to emerge at or near the somatic poles. This same tendency may be observed in other genera of poorly flagellated peritrichous bacteria and is not characteristic of rhizobia alone. A "monotrichous" individual may thus have a polar, a subpolar, or a lateral flagellum. By observing several individuals, one with a lateral flagellum or one with several flagella will usually be found and thus establish the flagellation as peritrichous. Another difference between the two types of flagellation is the flagellar wavelengths. The mean wavelengths of the normal subpolar flagella ranges from 1.9 microns to 2.2 microns, and of the peritrichous flagella from 1.3 microns to 1.6 microns.

Flagellar Variations

The peritrichous cultures showed no definite variations. The most striking variation was observed in the subpolar group. Strain 3I1b59 of the soybean group showed many individuals with one or more flagella with very short wavelength (curly) in addition to the normal flagellum. Strain 3I2b1 (from *Erythrina indica*) showed the same type of variants. In a few instances an organism was found with the curly flagella only. In most cases, however, the normal long wavelength flagellum was present. The curly flagella appeared to originate at the same locus as the normal flagellum. The wavelength of the curly flagella was very uniform, averaging 0.75 micron or about ⅓ that of the normal subpolar flagella.

TABLE IV

FLAGELLATION OF *Rhizobium* IN RELATION TO PHYTOPATHOGENICITY AND GROWTH RATE

Group	Host plant	Strains	Flagellation	Wavelength (microns)	Growth rate
Soybean	Glycina hispida	3	subpolar	2.06	+
Cowpea	Vigna sinensis	1	subpolar	2.00	+
	Erythrina indica	2	subpolar	2.0–2.7	+
	Phaseolus lunatus	9	subpolar	2.06	+
	Phaseolus lunatus	2	peritrichous	1.50	+++
	Phaseolus aureus	7	subpolar	2.07	+++
	Phaseolus angularis	1	subpolar	2.20	+++
	Phaseolus aconitifolius	2	subpolar	1.9–2.9	+
	Phaseolus acutifolius	5	subpolar	2.09	+
	Pueraria thunbergiana	3	subpolar	2.20	++
	Albizzia julibrissen	1	subpolar	2.00	+
	Albizzia julibrissen	1	peritrichous	1.0–1.6	+++
	Acacia linifola	1	peritrichous	1.60	+++
	Strophostyles pauciflora	2	peritrichous	1.46	++++
	Strophostyles helvola	3	peritrichous	1.60	+++
	Lupinus luteus	1	subpolar	—	+
	Lupinus angustifolius	1	subpolar	—	+
Lupine	Lupinus sp.	1	subpolar	2.05	+
	Lupinus densiflorus	3	peritrichous	1.52	+++
	Ulex europaeus	1	subpolar	2.08	+
Alfalfa	Medicago sativa	1	peritrichous	1.60	+++
	Medicago hispida	1	peritrichous	1.62	+++
	Melilotus alba	1	peritrichous	1.56	+++

TABLE IV (continued)

Group	Host plant	Strains	Flagellation	Wavelength (microns)	Growth rate
Clover	Trifolium dubium	1	peritrichous	1.2–1.4	+++
	Trifolium repens	1	peritrichous	1.50	+++
	Trifolium ambiguum	1	peritrichous	1.53	+++
Pea	Pisum arvense	2	peritrichous	1.30	+++
	Pisum sativum	1	peritrichous	1.35	+++
Bean	Phaseolus vulgaris	13	peritrichous	1.40	++++
	Lotus corniculatus	1	peritrichous	1.54	+++
	Lotus americanus	1	peritrichous	1.61	++
	Lotus uliginosus	1	?	0.75 (1.9)	+
	Caragana arborescens	2	peritrichous	1.52	+++
	Robinia pseudoacacia	2	peritrichous	1.54	+++
	Wisteria speciosa	1	subpolar	2.29	+
	Wisteria frutescens	1	peritrichous	1.2–1.7	++
	Amorpha fruticosa	1	peritrichous	1.67	+++

73

28. *Agrobacterium*

The genus *Agrobacterium* in Bergey's Manual is grouped together with *Rhizobium* and *Chromobacterium* in the family Rhizobiaceae. The more typical species of *Agrobacterium* such as *Agrobacterium tumefaciens, Agrobacterium rhizogenes,* and *Agrobacterium radiobacter* are very similar, both physiologically and morphologically, to the peritrichously flagellated species of *Rhizobium. Chromobacterium*, however, is so radically different that the author sees little justification for grouping it in the same family as *Agrobacterium* and *Rhizobium*.

CULTURES

Sixteen cultures of *Agrobacterium* were studied over a period of several years. Eight strains of various species came from Mortimer P. Starr of the University of California, two strains from Joel Hildebrant of the University of Wisconsin, and the others from various sources. All the cultures were carefully checked physiologically. Typical species of *Agrobacterium* oxidize, but do not ferment, carbohydrates. The oxidation of sucrose by these bacteria seems particularly noteworthy. With the exception of *Agrobacterium gypsophilae*, Starr TG-101, all cultures were physiologically typical of the genus. This culture of *A. gypsophilae* was a poorly flagellated, peritrichous rod which fermented carbohydrates. It could be a species of *Erwinia* but not *Agrobacterium*.

FLAGELLAR CHARACTERISTICS

The cultures studied were rather poorly flagellated with the majority of the individuals without flagella. One or two flagella per flagellated individual was most common with a few individuals having three to four flagella but rarely more. The arrangement of the flagella was peritrichous. In common with other poorly flagellated peritrichous rods the flagella show a strong tendency to originate at or near the somatic poles. The general appearance of the flagella of *A. tumefaciens, A. radiobacter,* and *A. rhizogenes* was very similar, and no variants were observed. The average wavelength of *A. tumefaciens* was 1.45 microns, of *A. radiobacter* 1.49 microns, and of *A. rhizogenes* 1.47 microns. These wave-

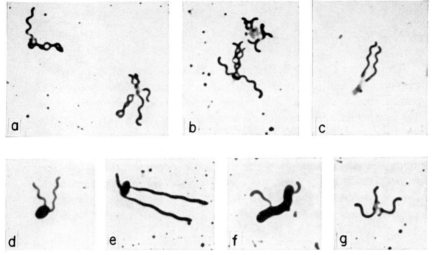

Fig. 30. a. *Agrobacterium tumefaciens*, Hildebrand strain. Peritrichous flagella of rather short wavelength. The organisms pictured are unusually well flagellated for *Agrobacterium* species.

b. *A. tumefaciens*, Starr TT-116. Peritrichous flagella of short wavelength as in a.

c. *A. rhizogenes*, NCIB 8196. Peritrichous flagellation very similar to that of *A. tumefaciens*. The flagella show a tendency to originate at or near the somatic pole, with the proximal part frequently straight as illustrated. This picture closely resembles some taken of the peritrichously flagellated rhizobia.

d. *A. radiobacter*, Starr TR-1. Peritrichous flagellation similar to that of *A. tumefaciens*.

e. *A. pseudotsugae*, Starr TP-102. Peritrichous flagella of relatively long wavelength and very small amplitude quite different from *A. tumefaciens*.

f. *A. pseudotsugae*, Starr TP-3. This strain was very poorly flagellated. Most of the flagella were very short with indefinite curvature.

g. *Agrobacterium* sp., Keller 72. This is one of several strains isolated from water and nothing is known about its phytopathogenicity. The flagellation is peritrichous with rather short flagella of distinctly greater wavelength than that of *A. tumefaciens*.

lengths correspond closely with those of the peritrichously flagellated rhizobia. *Agrobacterium pseudotsugae* had an entirely different type of flagella with much greater wavelength (2.4 microns) and unusually small amplitude. A culture isolated from water and physiologically typical of *Agrobacterium* also had flagella of distinctly different type from *A. tumefaciens*. The phytopathogenicity of this water strain is unknown. Two strains of *Agrobacterium rubi* studied did not show either motility or flagella. (See Fig. 30.)

29. *Chromobacterium*

The genus *Chromobacterium* has two characteristics by which it may be identified and differentiated from all other bacterial genera: the water insoluble purple pigment and the mixed polar and peritrichous flagellation. Physiologically the genus is heterogeneous, including psychrophiles and mesophiles, carbohydrate fermenters and nonfermenters. Opinions differ regarding the taxonomy of the genus but the author recognizes three species: *Chromobacterium violaceum*, *Chromobacterium manilae*, and *Chromobacterium laurentium* (Fig. 31). Twenty-eight selected cultures were studied, including several strains of each species.

FLAGELLAR CHARACTERISTICS

A polar, predominantly single, flagellum could be demonstrated in all strains. With some strains, particularly of *C. manilae*, the polar flagellum could not be stained with the standard flagella stain. Fairly satisfactory staining was obtained by the modified flagella stain with double the normal concentration of tannic acid. In addition to the polar flagellum, all but four strains showed a variable number of lateral flagella. The lateral flagella always stained readily with the standard stain. They differed from the polar flagella by having a much shorter wavelength. By plating the cultures in semisolid agar and fishing from the periphery of the most spreading colonies, the number of lateral flagella could be increased. The four strains which showed only polar flagella, however, did not show lateral flagella by this technique. The wavelength and amplitude of ten polar and of ten lateral flagella on as many individuals were measured. In Table V are recorded the mean values of these measurements.

FIG. 31. a, b, c, d, e. *Chromobacterium manilae*. Note the weakly stained polar flagellum, compared to the lateral flagella, in b, c and d. These polar flagella did not stain with the usual stain formula.

f. *C. violaceum*. A polar and a lateral flagellum of different wavelength.

g. *C. laurentium*. Mixed polar and peritrichous flagellation.

a–g. From E. Leifson, *J. Bacteriol.* **71**, 393-400 (1956).

76

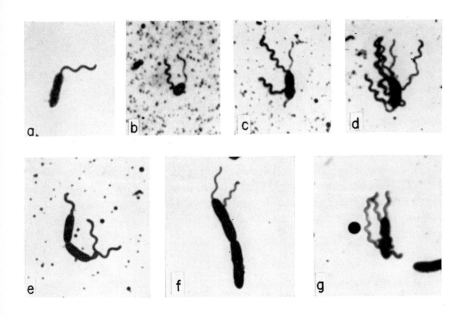

TABLE V

FLAGELLAR CHARACTERISTICS OF *Chromobacterium* SPECIES

| Species | Strains | Polar flagella | | | |
		Wave-length (microns)	SD[a]	Amplitude (microns)	SD
C. manilae	16	2.21	0.17	0.55	0.07
C. laurentium	6	2.07	0.13	0.52	0.07
C. violaceum	6	2.23	0.24	0.56	0.07
Genus mean		2.19[b]	0.18	0.54	0.07

| Species | Strains | Lateral flagella | | | |
		Wave-length (microns)	SD	Amplitude (microns)	SD
C. manilae	16	1.31	0.11	0.46	0.07
C. laurentium	6	1.35	0.07	0.43	0.06
C. violaceum	6	1.26	0.11	0.44	0.06
Genus mean		1.31[b]	0.10	0.45	0.06

[a] SD = standard deviation.

[b] $\dfrac{\text{WL polar flagella}}{\text{WL lateral flagella}} = \dfrac{2.19}{1.31} = 1.67.$

30. Sarcina

Two species of flagellated *Sarcina* are listed in Bergey's Manual. *Sarcina citrea* is described as producing a yellow to orange pigment, in the form of single individuals, pairs, and packets, and with a single flagellum per individual. A culture of this species could not be obtained. *Sarcina ureae* (*Sporosarcina ureae*) is a fairly common organism and three strains from different sources were studied. Namely: *Sporosarcina ureae* from C. B. van Niel, Hopkins Marine Station; *Sarcina ureae* from Bruce Stocker, London, England; and *Sarcina ureae* from Rudolph Hugh, George Washington University. All were morphologically typical and motile (Fig. 32).

FLAGELLAR CHARACTERISTICS

With an organism which characteristically occurs in packets of eight, and multiples of eight, the number of flagella per individual is difficult to determine. With packets which appear to consist of eight individuals the maximum number of flagella found was nine. A lesser number was more common. From this we may conclude that each individual coccus generally has only one flagellum. It is also very difficult to determine if a flagellum has a polar location, if one may use this term with *Sarcina*. No conclusion has been reached on this point and no opinion is ventured.

The flagella of *S. ureae* tend to be exceptionally long and the normal flagella have a greater wavelength than the great majority of normal flagella of rod shaped bacteria. Two of the strains studied showed normal flagella only. The third strain (Hugh) showed several shape variants: normal, curly, small amplitude, and one with a wavelength intermediate between normal and curly. This latter type is labeled subnormal and was only found in association with curly flagella on a packet. A few flagella were also found which were partly subnormal and partly curly. Attempts at isolation of pure cultures of the various flagellar types were not made.

The wavelength of the normal flagella of the three strains studied averaged 3.19 microns. The wavelength of the curly flagella averaged 1.4 microns. The few measurements possible on the subnormal wavelength averaged 2.3 microns. The small amplitude flagella had wavelengths averaging about 2 microns.

78

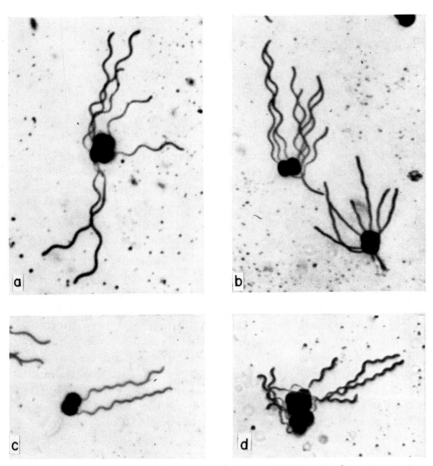

FIG. 32. a. *Sarcina* (*Sporosarcina*) *ureae*, L.E.1.1. Hopkins Marine Station. A packet of what appears to be eight cocci with seven normal flagella. This culture showed only normal flagella.

b. *Sarcina ureae*, Hugh. At the upper left is shown a packet of presumably eight cocci with eight normal flagella and one young flagellum without definite curvature. At the lower right is a packet of presumably eight cocci with seven long flagella, one medium-short and one very short. These flagella are of the small amplitude type.

c. *S. ureae*, Hugh. Note the lower flagellum of the packet with subnormal wavelength in the proximal portion and curly wavelength in the distal portion. In the upper left of the picture are the ends of normal flagella from other individuals.

d. *S. ureae*, Hugh. Illustrated are apparently two and possibly more packets of eight cocci each. The long flagella on the right are of the curly type. The relatively shorter flagellum in the upper right corner has the subnormal wavelength.

79

31. Streptococcus

The incidence of flagellated streptococci may not be as rare as it is commonly considered to be. Bacteriologists rarely examine a culture of cocci for motility, assuming it to be nonmotile. All flagellated streptococci studied to date fall in Lancefield group D, or the enterococcus group.

Three strains of motile streptococci were studied, one from Dr. O. Felsenfeld, Hektoen Institute, Chicago; and two from Dr. Hans Graudal, Statens Serum Institut, Copenhagen, Denmark.

FLAGELLAR CHARACTERISTICS

All three strains studied showed good motility and were well flagellated (see Fig. 33). The Felsenfeld strain showed a few fairly long chains while the Graudal strains showed mainly diplococci and rarely chains of as many as four individuals. In the Felsenfeld strain the individual organisms showed mainly one flagellum, occasionally two. The flagella appeared to originate most frequently at the point of division of two cells which may indicate a polar origin. The Graudal strains were definitely multitrichous with up to five flagella on a single cell. In these strains the flagella were definitely of polar origin in most instances. If one should characterize the flagellation in the usual terms the streptococci studied should probably be labeled polar multitrichous. If this is correct these streptococci are the only gram-positive bacteria with polar flagella ever encountered by the author.

The shape of the flagella in the three strains studied was mainly normal with unusually long wavelength, similar to *Sarcina ureae*. The normal wavelength of the three strains averaged 3.2 microns. In the Graudal strains were found a number of flagella which were partly curly. The wavelength of the curly waves averaged 1.2 microns. There was also found a rare flagellum with a wavelength about 2.4 microns which correspond to the subnormal type seen more distinctly in *Sarcina ureae*. The small amplitude shape seen in *Sarcina* was not found, nor were any other shapes found. In general, the shapes of the flagella of streptococci and *Sarcina* are quite similar and both types of cocci have normal flagella of distinctly longer wavelength than the great majority of rod shaped bacteria.

80

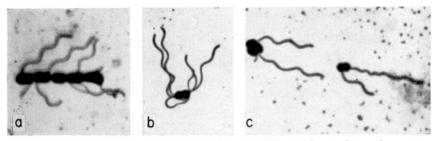

Fig. 33. a. *Streptococcus* sp., Type D, Felsenfeld. A chain of cocci in various stages of division. The exact origin of the flagella on the soma is not clear in this picture. The flagellar curvature is normal.

b. *Streptococcus* sp., Type O, Graudal. Two cocci showing distinctly polar multitrichous flagellation with flagella of normal curvature.

c. *Streptococcus* sp., Type D, Graudal. The pair of cocci on the right shows one flagellum in which the proximal portion is curly and the distal portion normal. This was very rare.

32. Lactobacillus

Motility in the genus *Lactobacillus* appears to be very rare and in Bergey's Manual all the species listed are described as nonmotile. A strain labeled *Lactobacillus plantarum* was received from Dr. P. Arne Hansen of the University of Maryland (Fig. 34).

Flagellar Characteristics

The culture studied was motile and fairly well flagellated with peritrichous flagella. No variants were seen. The curvature of the flagella was very uniform with an average wavelength of 2.26 microns and amplitude of 0.56 micron. Whatever phylogenetic relationship there may be between lactobacilli and streptococci to justify placing them in the same family is not apparent in the flagellation.

33. Corynebacterium

Reports of motility in the genus *Corynebacterium* appears limited to the phytopathogenic group and one cellulolytic organism variously labeled *Cellulomonas fimi* or *Corynebacterium fimi*. No systematic study was made of any other corynebacteria. One strain of *Corynebacterium fimi* was received from Dr. H. W. Reuszer of Purdue University. The following phytopathogens were furnished by Dr. Mortimer P. Starr of the University of California: *Corynebacterium tritici* (CT-102), *Corynebacterium michiganense* (CM-6), *Corynebacterium poinsettiae* (CP-1 and CP-42), *Corynebacterium flaccumfaciens* (CF-18 and CF-8). The phytopathogens studied were typical of the genus morphologically and physiologically. Three motile strains of *Corynebacterium citreum-mobile* were received from Dr. Werner Köhler in Germany. The three strains were culturally and morphologically identical. They produced a dark yellow pigment and grew readily on simple peptone media.

Flagellar Characteristics

C. tritici (CT-102) and *C. michiganense* (CM-6) were nonmotile and flagella could not be demonstrated. Strain CP-1 of *C. poinsettiae* was nonmotile and nonflagellated, but strain CP-42

82

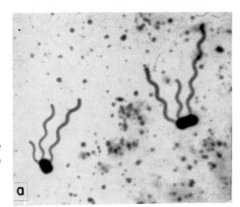

Fig. 34. a. *Lactobacillus plantarum*. Hansen strain. The flagella are peritrichous.

showed fair motility and about 1% or less of the individuals with flagella. The flagella were usually quite long and in no instance could more than one flagellum be found on one organism. The arrangement of the flagella was nonpolar (peritrichous). In all nonpolar or peritrichously flagellated bacteria there is a much greater proportion of the flagella located at or near the poles of the individuals than one would expect from chance. When dealing with bacteria which have many flagella per individual this is not so obvious as with bacteria having only one or two flagella per individual. An experienced observer may thus mistake nonpolar for polar flagellation. A polar flagellum usually emerges from the cell in line with the long axis of the soma of the bacterium while a nonpolar flagellum usually emerges at right angles to the soma. In *C. poinsettiae* CP-42 the flagellated individuals were monotrichous with most flagella located at or near the poles but the majority of the flagella emerged at right angles to the soma, and in a fair number the flagella emerged from the middle of the soma. *C. flaccumfaciens,* strains CF-8 and CF-18, were both motile and showed nonpolar (peritrichous) flagellation very similar to *C. poinsettiae.* These strains were mainly monotrichous but occasionally two flagella were found on one individual. *C. fimi,* Reuszer strain, was motile though very poorly flagellated. The flagella were nonpolar (peritrichous) in arrangement. As with the phytopathogens the majority of the cells were monotrichous but with this organism a fair number of cells showed two flagella and a rare individual had three flagella. The Koehler strains showed the same flagellar arrangement as the phytopathogens. In these strains individuals with two flagella were fairly common.

The flagella of *C. fimi* and the Koehler strains showed a much greater wavelength than the flagella of the phytopathogens, as indicated in Table VI and also obvious from the illustrations (Fig. 35). Of some significance perhaps is the difference in wavelengths of the two strains of *C. flaccumfaciens.* These differences are statistically significant. Strain CF-18 of *C. flaccumfaciens* produced acid in inulin and raffinose while strain CF-8 did not.

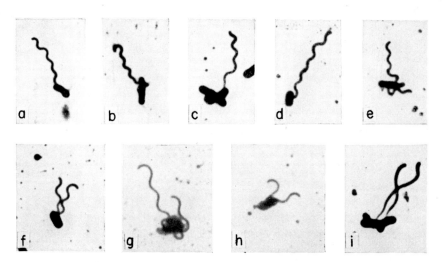

FIG. 35. a, b, c, d, e. *Corynebacterium flaccumfaciens*, Starr CF-18. These figures illustrate the typical flagellation of *C. flaccumfaciens*. More than one flagellum per individual is extremely rare. The flagellum usually originates at or near the somatic pole but should not be confused with polar flagellation.

f. *C. poinsettiae*, Starr CP-42. Most individuals in this culture showed only one flagellum, if any. The flagellar arrangement was definitely peritrichous and similar to that of *C. flaccumfaciens*.

g, h. *Corynebacterium* (*Cellulomonas*) *fimi*, Reuszer 133. The flagella are peritrichously arranged and of rather long wavelength.

i. *C. citreum-mobile*, Koehler. The majority of the flagellated individuals in this culture had only one flagellum. The arrangement was peritrichous like the phytopathogens. Note the long wavelength similar to *C. fimi*.

TABLE VI

MEAN WAVELENGTHS OF *Corynebacterium* SPECIES

Species	Wavelength (Microns)
C. poinsettiae, CP-42	2.09
C. flaccumfaciens, CF-8	2.17
C. flaccumfaciens, CF-18	1.74
C. fimi, Reuszer 133	3.0
C. citreum-mobile, Koehler	3.16

34. *Arthrobacter*

One culture labeled *Arthrobacter citreus* was received from Dr. L. E. Sacks of U.S.D.A., Albany, California (Fig. 36). The culture grew well on simple media with a lemon yellow, water insoluble pigment. The organism was gram positive, very pleomorphic and showed some motility in moist preparation. The motility was nonprogressive and consisted mainly of spinning and wiggling.

FLAGELLAR CHARACTERISTICS

The one culture of *A. citreus* examined showed mainly straight flagella (or very small amplitude flagella) with nonpolar or peritrichous arrangement. Most individuals showed only one flagellum. One organism only was seen with a normal flagellum. However, reports in the literature show *Arthrobacter simplex* with both normal (wavelength about 2 microns) and curly (wavelength about 1 micron) flagella so the strain of *A. citreus* studied may not have had the most typical flagellation of the genus.

35. *Listeria*

All strains of *Listeria* are classified into the one species *Listeria monocytogenes*. The organism is peritrichously flagellated, and well flagellated if cultured at low temperatures such as 20° C., but very poorly flagellated if cultured at 37° C. At 38° C. flagella are not produced. In cultures at 37° C. a single flagellum may be found on a small proportion of the organisms which led to the early reports that the organism was polar monotrichous.

Of all the bacteria the author has encountered *Listeria* has shown the greatest genetic instability, or mutability, in regard to flagellar shape and function (see Fig. 37). This apparent mutability may partly be due to the fact that a large number of strains (eighty-one) were studied, since a large proportion (85%) of the strains did not show any variants. The cultures were all old stock strains and this in itself appears to contribute to genetic instability. All of the cultures included in this study were received from Dr. A. M. Griffin of George Washington University.

FLAGELLAR CHARACTERISTICS

The flagella of *Listeria* showed four distinct shapes: normal, small amplitude, straight, and coiled. Variants with each type of flagella were isolated in pure culture. Curiously enough the var-

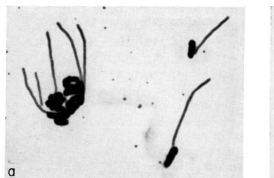 

Fig. 36. a. *Arthrobacter citreus,* Sacks. This figure shows the most common flagellation of the culture studied. The flagella were straight or with a slight curvature (small amplitude), and usually single. The arrangement was peritrichous.

b. *A. citreus,* Sacks. This was the only organism seen on the slide with a normal flagellum.

iant flagellar shape most often encountered in other bacteria, namely the curly shape, was not observed in *Listeria,* nor could the curly shape be induced by lowering the pH. Filamentous variants could readily be obtained and these invariably retained the flagellar shape of the parent nonfilamentous type. The normal flagellar shape was by far the most common and was present in all of the eighty motile strains studied.

The flagella of *Listeria* also showed variations in function. One of the original cultures had normal flagella but was entirely non-motile. From two other cultures were isolated pure strains of normal flagellated nonmotile individuals. Organisms with the coiled flagellar shape showed fair motility but those with small amplitude and straight flagella showed very poor motility at best and no progressive motion at all. Two variants with straight flagella were obtained, one of which was entirely nonmotile while the other showed only a nonprogressive wiggling and spinning motion.

On the basis of flagellar shape and function, seven varieties of individuals were obtained in pure culture: nonflagellated; normal flagella, motile and nonmotile; straight flagella, motile (very slight) and nonmotile; coiled flagella, fair motility; small amplitude flagella, slight motility. By plating in semisolid agar a variety of flagellar mutations were observed but no new types found. The rate of such mutations were calculated to be in the neighborhood of 10^{-8} to 10^{-9} per cell division.

The normal wavelength and amplitude of different strains showed only minor differences. From 10 measurements on each of eight strains was obtained an average wavelength of 2.01 microns with a standard deviation (S.D.) of 0.1 micron, and an average amplitude of 0.48 micron with an S.D. of 0.06 micron. Based on 20 measurements the wavelength of the small amplitude flagella was 1.53 microns with amplitude 0.25 micron. For the coiled flagella the wavelength was 2.18 microns and the amplitude 0.76 micron.

Fig. 37. a. *Listeria monocytogenes.* Normal flagella, peritrichous arrangement.
    b. *L. monocytogenes.* Small amplitude flagella.
    c. *L. monocytogenes.* Straight flagella.
    d. *L. monocytogenes.* Coiled flagella.
    e. *L. monocytogenes.* Normal flagella. Filamentous soma.
    f. *L. monocytogenes.* Straight flagella. Filamentous soma.
    g. *L. monocytogenes.* Coiled flagella. Filamentous soma.
    a–e. From E. Leifson, and M. I. Palen, *J. Bacteriol.* **70**, 233-240 (1955).

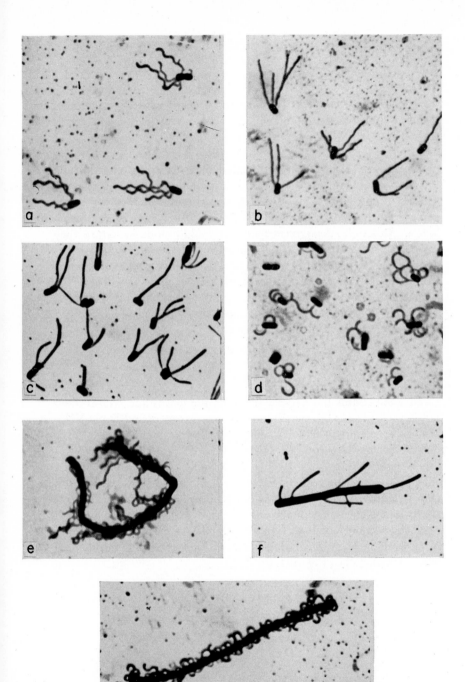

36. *Alcaligenes*

The genus *Alcaligenes* is composed of peritrichously flagellated bacteria and related nonflagellated types which do not attack carbohydrates. Many types of polar flagellated bacteria have cultural and physiological characteristics very similar to *Alcaligenes* species. These polar flagellated bacteria are often mistaken for *Alcaligenes* and are found in culture collections as *Alcaligenes* species of one kind or another. It is impossible to identify an organism as *Alcaligenes* without determining the nature of the flagellation. Although *Alcaligenes* species are ubiquitous in nature they are not as common as most bacteriologists believe. The author has studied a fair number of strains of *Alcaligenes* obtained from a variety of sources over a period of several years. Most of the species listed in Bergey's Manual are unidentifiable and should be discarded. The author includes *Alcaligenes* (*Brucella, Bordetella*) *bronchisepticus* in the genus because of its similar morphological and physiological characteristics.

FLAGELLAR CHARACTERISTICS

In some strains the flagella are quite numerous and well-formed but in most strains the flagellation is only fair or poor (Table VII). The most common flagellar shape is the normal and the only definite other shape found was the curly. All strains of *Alcaligenes bronchisepticus* studied, twenty in number, had normal flagella only, and so did the two strains studied of *Alcaligenes denitrificans*. One strain of *Alcaligenes faecalis* had only curly flagella and one strain had some individuals with normal flagella and some with curly flagella but not both types of flagella on the same individual. A peritrichously flagellated mutant of *Lophomonas faecalis* had only curly flagella (Fig. 38).

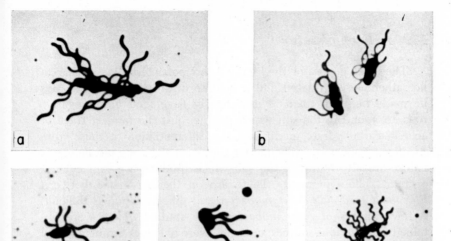

Fig. 38. a. *Alcaligenes faecalis,* H-222. Two unusually well-flagellated organisms showing normal flagella peritrichously arranged.

b. *A. faecalis,* H-136. Peritrichous flagella showing some coiling tendency.

c. *A. denitrificans,* H-12. Normal flagella, peritrichously arranged.

d. *A. bronchisepticus,* H-184. Peritrichous flagella of normal curvature.

e. *A. faecalis,* H-247. This is a mutant of *Lophomonas faecalis.* Curly, peritrichous flagella.

c. From E. Leifson, and R. Hugh, *J. Gen. Microbiol.* **11,** 512-513 (1954).

e. From E. Leifson, and R. Hugh, *J. Bacteriol.* **65,** 263-271 (1953).

(See p. 93 for Table VII.)

37. *Achromobacter*

The three genera of the family Achromobacteriaceae appear to be rather closely related and a definite distinction cannot always be made between them. Peritrichously flagellated gram-negative rods are found in the soil which produce just the faintest trace of acid in carbohydrate media and the differentiation of these from *Alcaligenes* species is difficult. Organisms of the same physiological nature are also found in the soil which produce a cream colored or faint yellow pigment. These are on the borderline between *Flavobacterium* and *Achromobacter* and differentiation is difficult. A few cultures of *Achromobacter* were studied. They were obtained from various sources and some were old stock strains labeled *Alcaligenes*. Much can be said in favor of combining *Alcaligenes* and *Achromobacter* into one genus.

FLAGELLAR CHARACTERISTICS

All of the more typical cultures studied had peritrichous flagella with normal curvature (Fig. 39). The flagellation was generally fair to poor. The average wavelength of the strains studied was 2.39 microns.

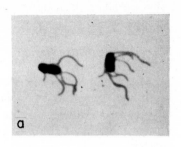

Fig. 39. a. *Achromobacter* sp., H-137. Typical normal peritrichous flagella. The flagellar shape in most strains studied was quite irregular.

TABLE VII
Mean Flagellar Wavelengths of *Alcaligenes* Species

Species	Strain	Wavelength (microns) Normal	Curly
A. *bronchisepticus*	H-46	2.70	
	H-47	2.76	
	H-48	2.68	
	H-49	2.85	
	H-50	2.76	
	H-51	2.87	
	H-52	2.73	
	H-140	2.86	
	H-171	2.86	
	H-180	3.04	
	H-181	2.65	
	H-182	2.58	
	H-183	2.62	
	H-184	2.50	
	H-225	2.82	
	H-227	2.89	
	H-232	2.96	
	Species mean	2.78	
A. *denitrificans*	H-12	2.74	—
	H-13	2.64	—
	Species mean	2.69	
A. *faecalis*	H-135	2.82	—
	H-138	2.24	1.07
	H-222	2.58	—
	H-223	—	1.29
	H-247	—	1.03
	Species mean	2.55	1.13
	Genus mean	2.67	1.13

38. *Flavobacterium*

The genus *Flavobacterium* is characterized by a yellow water-insoluble pigment and peritrichous flagellation, if any. Some strain have a weak oxidative action on carbohydrates, others have none. Many unidentified cultures were studied as well as several named species.

FLAGELLAR CHARACTERISTICS

The only well flagellated culture studied was an unnamed but typical species received from Dr. J. D. Stout of New Zealand. This organism was rather filamentous with numerous curly peritrichous flagella as illustrated in Fig. 40f. Five named cultures were received from Dr. Owen D. Weeks of the University of Idaho. Only two of these were flagellated: *Flavobacterium marinotypicum*, Zobell (F-6), showed poor flagellation with only one nonpolar flagellum per flagellated organism as illustrated in Fig. 40a. The single flagellum had an average wavelength of 2.5 microns but many were coiled. *Flavobacterium suaveolens*, ATCC (F-23), showed fair flagellation with one or two flagella per organism as illustrated in Fig. 40b. The majority of the flagella had an average wavelength of 1.85 microns. Two flagellated cultures typical of the genus were received from Dr. Oleg Lysenko of Yugoslavia: *Flavobacterium* sp., BmEl, was isolated from *Bombex mori* and was peritrichously flagellated as illustrated in Fig. 40d. Both normal flagella, with an average wavelength of 2.9 microns, and curly flagella, with an average wavelength of 1.4 microns, were found on the same and on separate organisms. *Flavobacterium* sp., Ac21, was isolated from *Aporya crataegi*. The flagellation was fair with normal peritrichous flagella of average wavelength of 2.95 microns as illustrated in Figs. 40c, e.

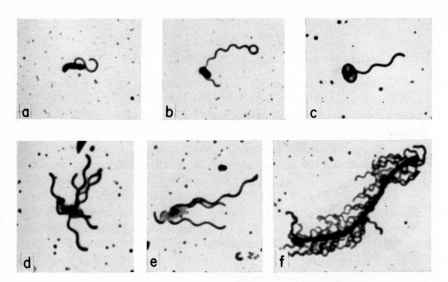

Fig. 40. a. *Flavobacterium marinotypicum,* Zobell (F-6). A nonpolar flagellum of rather long wavelength. Coiled flagella were common in this culture.

b. *F. suaveolens,* ATCC (F-23). Peritrichous flagella of normal but somewhat short wavelength.

c, e. *Flavobacterium* sp., Lysenko Ac21. Peritrichous flagella of normal shape and rather long wavelength.

d. *Flavobacterium* sp., Lysenko BmE1. Peritrichous flagella of normal shape.

f. *Flavobacterium* sp., Stout K-8. Peritrichous flagellation. This culture showed only the curly type of flagella. Most individuals were filamentous.

39. *Cellulomonas*

Cellulomonas is the generic name commonly used for a group of gram-negative, simple rods which decompose cellulose. The generic name is unfortunate since these bacteria show peritrichous flagellation.

Six strains labeled *Cellulomonas* were studied. Five of these were supplied by Dr. H. W. Reuszer of Purdue University, and one (*Cellulomonas biazotea*) was supplied by William C. Haynes of the Northern Regional Research Laboratory, U.S.D.A., Peoria, Illinois. Two cultures failed to show either motility or flagella: *C. biazotea*, NRRL B-401, and *Cellulomonas cellasea*, Reuszer 124. One strain was labeled *Cellulomonas fima*, Reuszer 133, and is discussed under *Corynebacterium*. The other three strains showed good to fair flagellation and motility.

Flagellar Characteristics

Cellulomonas rossica, Reuszer 128, grew well on simple media, produced colorless growth, and was very motile. Flagellation was good with many normal peritrichous flagella per individual. No variants were observed. *Cellulomonas bibula* grew well on simple media with a yellow pigmentation. Flagellation was good but each individual seldom showed more than one flagellum with peritrichous arrangement. The curvature of the flagella was pure curly except for a rare flagellum with the proximal end of very long wavelength (approximately 2.8 microns) and the distal end curly. *Cellulomonas perlurida* showed moderate growth with spots of yellow on agar media. Flagellation was fair, with most individuals having only one flagellum and a few with two or more. Most individuals showed pure curly peritrichous flagella. A few individuals showed normal peritrichous flagella. Also in this strain were observed flagella with proximal end normal and distal end curly. One organism was observed with a long normal flagellum and a short curly flagellum. Morphologically *C. bibula* and *C. perlurida* were similar, while *Cellulomonas rossica* was quite different. The normal flagella of *C. rossica* had an average wavelength of 2.1 microns. Curly flagella were not observed in *C. rossica*. The curly flagella of *C. bibula* and *C. perlurida* averaged 1.06 and 1.05 microns, respectively. The normal flagella of *C.*

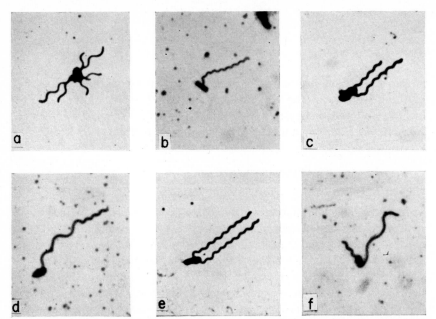

FIG. 41. a. *Cellulomonas rossica,* Reuszer. Normal, peritrichous flagella.

b, c. *C. bibula,* Reuszer. A single curly flagellum was most common but individuals were also seen with several curly flagella. The arrangement is peritrichous.

d. *C. perlurida,* Reuszer. This shows a flagellum with the proximal end of normal curvature and the distal end curly. The wavelength ratio of the normal and curly waves is about 3:1. Normal wavelength, 2.9 microns, curly wavelength, 1.05 microns.

e. *C. perlurida,* Reuszer. Long curly flagella, peritrichously arranged.

f. *C. perlurida,* Reuszer. A normal and a curly flagellum on same individual.

perlurida had an average wavelength of 2.9 microns and those of *C. bibula* 2.8 microns. (See Fig. 41.) Morphologically *C. perlurida* and *C. bibula* appear to be identical and could well be considered a species of the genus *Flavobacterium.*

97

40. *Escherichia*

Several dozen strains of *Escherichia* have been studied. Most of these were from the collection of Dr. MacDonald Fulton and included all the common physiological types of *Escherichia coli*, *Escherichia freundii*, and the slow lactose fermenting paracolons.

FLAGELLAR CHARACTERISTICS

All strains showed peritrichous arrangement of the flagella (Fig. 42). The flagellation of the colon bacilli is quite variable with atrichous and poorly flagellated strains very common. With most motile cultures the flagellation can be greatly improved by culture in semisolid agar and fishing from the periphery of the spreading growth. Most strains studied showed normal flagella only. A few strains showed both normal and curly flagellated individuals. Individuals with both normal and curly flagella were extremely rare and in no instance could the normal curvature be changed to the curly by lowering the pH. In this respect the coliforms are like *Salmonella* but unlike *Proteus*. Some strains may show a considerable proportion of coiled flagella.

The mean wavelength of the normal flagella of fifteen strains of *Escherichia* was 2.74 microns. Only one strain with curly flagella was found and the wavelength was 1.15 microns. In Table VIII are given the mean flagellar wavelengths of various genera in the enteric group.

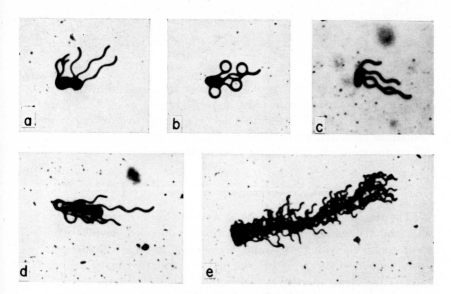

Fig. 42. a. *Escherichia coli*, F-3412. Peritrichous flagella of normal shape. The flagellation of *Escherichia* strains tends to be rather poor. Coiled and irregularly curved flagella are common. Strains with curly flagella are occasionally encountered.

b. Paracolon type (Bethesda), F-364. This shows a normal flagellum extending out from the somatic pole and four nicely coiled flagella. The organisms of the paracolon group have much the same type of flagellation as the typical *Escherichia*.

c. Paracolon type (Arizona). Peritrichous flagella of normal curvature.

d, e. *E. freundii*, F-360. In d is illustrated the normal peritrichous flagella. In e is shown a filamentous form with curly flagella. Curly flagella, of course, are also found on nonfilamentous individuals.

(See p. 101 for Table VIII.)

41. Aerobacter

All the flagellated strains of *Aerobacter* are classified in the one species, *Aerobacter cloacae* (Fig. 43). Eight strains of *A. cloacae* were received from Dr. Sverre Dick Henrikson in Norway, and one strain from Dr. Perry Wilson of the University of Wisconsin. All strains were physiologically typical and motile.

FLAGELLAR CHARACTERISTICS

The flagellation of *A. cloacae* is very similar to that of *Escherichia* and the paracolon group. Normal and coiled flagella were most common, with two strains showing a few individuals with curly flagella. Change in pH did not change the flagellar curvature. The average normal wavelength for the ten strains was 2.77 microns, with a range of 2.59 to 2.90 microns. The curly flagellar wavelengths averaged 1.17 microns. These wavelengths are not significantly different from those of *Escherichia* and the paracolon group as shown in Table VIII.

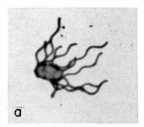 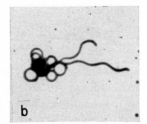 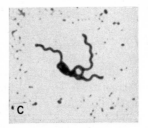

FIG. 43. a. *Aerobacter cloacae*, F-3942. Normal peritrichous flagella.
b. *A. cloacae*, F-3784. Normal and coiled flagella.
c. *A. cloacae*, F-3943. This individual shows two partly curly flagella, one coiled flagellum and one normal flagellum. Curly flagella were seldom seen in this species.

TABLE VIII

FLAGELLAR WAVELENGTHS OF THE ENTERIC GROUP

Group	Number of strains	Range of wavelength (microns)	
		Normal	Curly
Escherichia	15	2.59–3.02	—
Paracolon	31	2.58–2.88	0.87–1.20
Aerobacter	9	2.59–2.90	—
Erwinia[a]	33	2.31–3.02	1.06–1.35
Salmonella[b]	39	2.30–2.71	1.12–1.15
Proteus	60	2.13–2.39	1.06–1.16

Group	Number of strains	Mean wavelength (microns)	
		Normal	Curly
Escherichia	15	2.74	1.15 (1 strain)
Paracolon	31	2.68	1.08 (6 strains)
Aerobacter	9	2.77	1.17 (2 strains)
Erwinia[a]	33	2.72	1.20 (9 strains)
Salmonella[b]	39	2.51	1.13 (3 strains)
Proteus	60	2.26	1.10 (40 strains)

[a] The mean normal wavelengths of the coliform group and *Erwinia* are not significantly different.

[b] The mean normal wavelengths of *Salmonella* differ significantly from the coliform group *Erwinia* and *Proteus*. The mean curly wavelengths of all groups do not differ significantly.

101

42. Erwinia

The genus *Erwinia* is composed of a group of phytopathogenic bacteria closely related to the coliform group. Should any organism of this genus be isolated in the ordinary public health or clinical laboratory it would certainly be considered a type of coliform.

CULTURES

A total of fifty-four cultures representing fifteen named species were studied physiologically and morphologically. The great majority of these cultures were received from Dr. Mortimer P. Starr of the University of California. A few cultures were from N. A. Smith, U.S.D.A., and a few from various sources. All cultures grew readily at 20° C. in simple peptone media with the exception of *Erwinia tracheiphila*. Four strains of this latter organism were studied. All grew slowly and relatively poorly, and were nonmotile and nonflagellated. Many of the other strains studied were

---

FIG. 44. a. *Erwinia amylovora*, EA-145. A short filament with normal peritrichous flagella.

b. *E. amylovora*, EA-11. A rather unusual situation in this species with normal and curly flagella on the same organism.

c. *E. amylovora*, EA-128. A short filament with coiled flagella mainly.

d. *E. salicis*, ES-4. This culture showed only normal flagella.

e. *Erwinia* sp., Walnut, WC-1. An exceptionally well flagellated culture showing normal flagella only.

f. *E. lathryi*, EL-102. Beautifully flagellated culture with normal flagella only.

g. *E. carotovora*, EC-153. Rather short normal flagella typical of this strain.

h. *E. carotovora*, EC-109. This organism shows one curly flagellum and several normal ones. This culture showed a mixture of individuals with only normal and only curly flagella. The organism pictured was one of a very few with both types of flagella.

i. *E. chrysanthemi*, EC-176. This species showed mainly coiled flagella. The organism pictured shows mixed coiled and curly flagella which was common in this strain.

j. *E. aroideae*, EA-148. A pure curly individual. This strain also showed individuals with normal flagella and mixed normal and curly flagella.

k. *E. solanisapra*, ES-3. This strain showed normal flagella only which did not change to curly by acid suspension.

l. *E. solanisapra*, ES-101. This culture showed only curly flagella. It was labeled nonmotile by the donor. Moist preparation showed nonprogressive wiggling and turning motion.

102

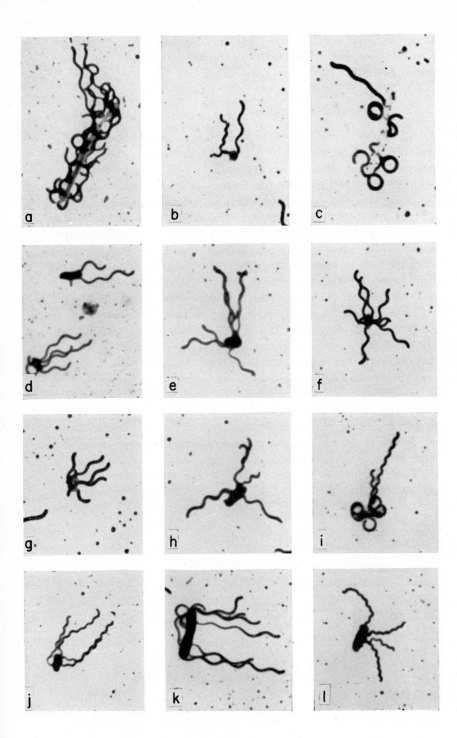

nonmotile and nonflagellated but in only one species, *Erwinia phytophthora* (in addition to *E. tracheiphila*) were no motile strains found.

FLAGELLAR CHARACTERISTICS

All of the motile strains studied showed peritrichous flagellation. From the standpoint of flagellation the genus is very heterogeneous. Some species have flagella resembling those of the coliform group, others resemble *Proteus*. The most common flagellar shape was the normal with several species showing only this shape. The curly shape was fairly common. One strain of *Erwinia solanisapra*, ES-101, was completely curly, while another strain of the same species, ES-3, was completely normal. It is interesting to note that the donor of the culture described *E. solanisapra*, ES-101, as being nonmotile. Careful observation of this culture in moist preparation did show some motility but only a nonprogressive wiggling and turning motion. *Erwinia aroideae*, EA-8, was mainly curly. Two species, *Erwinia atroseptica*, EA-112, and *Erwinia nimipressuralis*, EN-1, showed only normal flagella in alkaline suspension and mainly curly flagella in slightly acid suspension. The coiled shape was found to a variable extent in several species. One strain of *Erwinia amylovora* showed a great deal of coiling. Three strains of *Erwinia chrysanthemi* had mainly coiled flagella with some curly and normal flagella mixed in. Mixed curly and normal, curly and coiled, normal and coiled were found in several strains. (See Fig. 44.)

Table IX gives a summary of the morphological characteristics of the strains studied. The organisms are grouped according to the pathology they produce: dry necrosis, soft rot, and non-pectolytic.

104

TABLE IX

FLAGELLAR CHARACTERISTICS OF *Erwinia* SPECIES

Pathology	Species	Strains studied	Flagella wavelength (microns)	
			Normal[a]	Curly[a]
Dry necrosis	*E. amylovora*	6	2.77	1.20
	E. amylovora, f. var. *rubi*	1	3.02	1.35
	E. salicis	1	2.74	—
	E. tracheiphila	4	—	—
	Erwinia sp. (Walnut)	2	2.81	—
Soft rot	*E. aroideae*	2	2.85	1.26
	E. atroseptica	2	2.73	1.20
	E. carotovora	2	2.58	1.15
	E. carotovora f. var. *parthenii*	1	2.69	—
	E. phytophthora	1	—	—
	E. solanisapra	3	2.80	1.06
Non-pectolytic	*E. ananas*	3	2.44	—
	E. cypripedii	2	2.56	1.16
	E. lathryi	1	2.61	—
	E. milletiae	1	2.91	—
	E. nimipressuralis	1	2.31	1.16
	E. rhapontica	2	3.0 ±	—
	E. chrysanthemi	3	2.74	1.23

[a] Genus mean wavelength: normal = 2.72, curly = 1.20.

105

43. *Serratia*

Species of the genus *Serratia* generally produce a characteristic red pigment. Colorless variants are common and these are difficult to identify with certainty. The genus has been separated into several species but the differences between these species is not great and bacteriologists in general tend to label any red pigmented gram negative rod with the proper physiological characteristics as *Serratia marcescens*.

Eight strains labeled *S. marcescens* were studied. Three of these came from Dr. MacDonald Fulton and were isolated from clinical material. The other five strains were of diverse origin and came from the National Collection of Industrial Bacteria in England. All these strains were pigmented and physiologically typical of the genus. From the American Type Culture Collection were obtained five cultures which appeared typical of the genus: *Serratia kiliensis* 992, *Serratia plymuthica* 183, and *Serratia indica* 4002 were well flagellated; *S. indica* 4003 and *Serratia urinae* 11111 were nonflagellated. From W. B. Haynes of NRRL were obtained two cultures: *Serratia anolium* B-1700 was well flagellated and physiologically typical except for lack of pigmentation; *S. indica* B-341 was nonflagellated.

Flagellar Characteristics

Three of the fifteen cultures studied were nonflagellated which would indicate that nonflagellated variants of *Serratia* are fairly common. With one exception the flagellated strains showed more or less identical flagellation with coiled peritrichous flagella. From an occasional uncoiled flagellum a mean wavelength of 4.5 microns was obtained. In *S. marcescens*, NCIB 2302, was seen a flagellum which was curly in its proximal part with a coil at the end. This organism is illustrated in Fig. 45a. The curly waves measured 1.1 microns. The culture of *S. indica*, NCIB 4002, showed two types of individuals, one with the typical coiled flagella and one with normal peritrichous flagella. On plating a culture was obtained with organisms having normal flagella only. This culture was physiologically typical of the genus. The wavelength of the normal flagella averaged 2.3 microns.

106

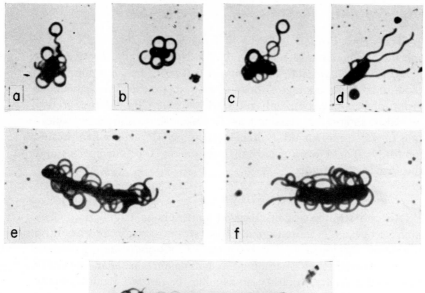

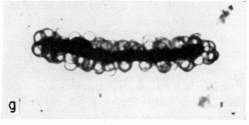

FIG. 45. a. *Serratia marcescens,* NCIB 3202. Typical coiled peritrichous flagella with one flagellum curly in its proximal part, ending in a coil.

b. *S. anolium,* NRRL B-1700. Typical coiled peritrichous flagella.

c, d. *S. indica,* NCIB 4002. This culture was a mixture of organisms with the coiled flagella typical of the genus, illustrated in c, and normal flagella, illustrated in d. By plating, a pure culture with normal flagella was obtained.

e. *S. plymuthica,* ATCC 183. A short filament with the typical coiled peritrichous flagella.

f. *S. kiliensis,* ATCC 992. A short filament with typical coiled peritrichous flagella.

g. *S. marcescens,* NCIB 2302. The filamentous form of this organism with typical coiled peritrichous flagella.

a–g. From M. Fulton, C. Forney, and E. Leifson, *Can. J. Microbiol.* **5**, 269-275 (1959).

44. *Proteus*

The genus *Proteus* is fairly well defined physiologically. Four species are commonly recognized: *Proteus mirabilis, Proteus vulgaris, Proteus morganii,* and *Proteus rettgeri.* The last named of these has some characteristics relating it to the *Salmonella.* A group of bacteria commonly referred to as the "Providence group" probably should be classified as *Proteus.* From the large collection of Dr. MacDonald Fulton were selected seventy-five strains for study. These were evenly divided among the four species and the Providence group.

Flagellar Characteristics

All the strains studied showed peritrichous flagellation. The number of flagella varied greatly from strain to strain and has little taxonomic significance. The cultures of *P. mirabilis* and *P. vulgaris* which showed the "swarming" phenomenon on agar generally showed the greatest density of flagella. *P. rettgeri* strains usually showed the fewest flagella.

Normal and curly flagella were observed in all strains studied with the exception of *P. rettgeri.* In this species only one of the twelve strains studied showed an occasional curly flagellum. As may be seen in the illustrations (Fig. 46), an individual organism

---

Fig. 46. a, b. *Proteus mirabilis,* Fulton 52. In a is illustrated the typical normal peritrichous flagella of *Proteus.* In b is shown the corresponding curly flagella on the same strain. The organism in a was stained from a slightly alkaline suspension while that in b from a slightly acid suspension, both from the same culture.

c. *P. vulgaris.* Mainly coiled flagella with two normal flagella at the top of the soma.

d. *Proteus* sp., Providence type. Semicoiled flagella. These were quite rare in the *Proteus* group and have not been definitely observed in other kinds of bacteria.

e. *P. morganii.* Normal and curly flagella on the same individual.

f. *P. mirabilis.* Many curly flagella and one normal flagellum on the same individual. These mixed types of flagellation were seen mainly in slides prepared from suspensions at pH 6.5 to 7.5.

g, h, i, j. *P. morganii.* These figures show various double curvature arrangements: proximal end curly, distal normal; proximal normal, distal curly; ends normal, center curly; alternating normal and curly.

k. *P. mirabilis,* Fulton 52. A filamentous form with mainly normal flagella. A curly flagellum may be seen on the right end.

a–j. From E. Leifson, S. R. Carhart, and M. Fulton, *J. Bacteriol.* **69**, 73-82 (1955).

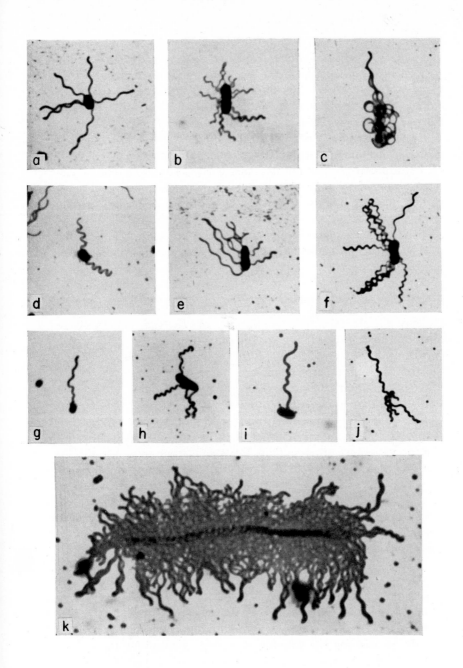

109

may show only normal flagella, only curly flagella, or mixed curly and normal. Occasionally a flagellum may be part normal and part curly in various arrangements. Most *Proteus* flagella, except those of *P. rettgeri,* assume the normal shape in media above pH 7.5 and the curly shape in media below pH 6.5. At a pH between 6.5 and 7.5 the flagellation tends to be mixed normal and curly. This pH sensitivity is not unique for *Proteus* but is also found to a limited extent in *Erwinia, Azotobacter,* and *Bacillus.*

In addition to the normal and curly shapes, coiled flagella were observed to a variable extent in all species, absent in some strains but common in others. In the Providence group, and in some strains of *P. morganii,* a very few organisms showed the semicoiled shape. The semicoiled flagella are very characteristic having an exceptionally large amplitude in relation to the wavelength.

Flagellar Measurements

The wavelengths and amplitudes of *Proteus* flagella were measured to a great extent. In Table X are summarized the mean wavelengths and amplitudes of the normal and curly flagella of the sixty best flagellated strains. Studies were also made of the effect of variation in culture medium, age of culture, etc. These studies showed remarkably little variation in wavelength and amplitude in different media and at different ages of culture. In summarizing the statistical data it may be stated: statistically significant variations are found in the mean strain wavelengths indicating that a species in *Proteus* is not morphologically homogeneous. The mean wavelengths of normal flagella of *P. mirabilis, P. vulgaris,* and *P. morganii* do not differ significantly but do differ significantly from the mean wavelengths of *P. morganii* (trehalose +), *P. rettgeri,* and the Providence group. The mean spiral unit lengths

$$\text{S.U.L.} = \sqrt{\text{WL}^2 + \text{Amp}^2 \pi^2}$$

were not significantly different except for *P. rettgeri* which was greater. Again *P. rettgeri* appears different from the others. The curly flagella of all strains were of quite uniform wavelength, being slightly greater for the Providence group. *P. rettgeri* showed so few curly flagella that it could not be compared with the others.

110

TABLE X
Flagellar Characteristics of *Proteus* Species[a]

Species	Normal flagella					Curly flagella				
	Strains	Wavelength (microns)	SD	Amplitude (microns)	SD	Strains	Wavelength (microns)	SD	Amplitude (microns)	SD
P. mirabilis	8	2.13	0.06[b]	0.60	0.09	8	1.06	0.02	0.42	0.13
P. vulgaris	8	2.25	0.21	0.48	0.05	8	1.07	0.04	0.36	0.03
P. morganii	10	2.14	0.15	0.57	0.09	10	1.11	0.07	0.39	0.05
P. morganii (trehalose +)	9	2.34	0.17	0.50	0.09	9	1.11	0.10	0.39	0.09
Providence group	13	2.31	0.11	0.53	0.02	5	1.16	0.04	0.35	0.05
P. rettgeri	12	2.39	0.08	0.61	0.05	0	—	—	—	—
Genus mean	60	2.26	0.19[c]	0.55		40	1.10	0.08	0.38	—

a From E. Leifson, S. R. Carhart, and M. Fulton, *J. Bacteriol.* **69**, 73-82 (1955).
b Standard deviation of strain means from species mean.
c Standard deviation of species means from genus mean.

45. *Salmonella*

With the exception of a few well recognized types such as *Salmonella gallinarum* and *Salmonella pullorum,* species or types of *Salmonella* are generally motile and flagellated. The flagellation of a large number of strains of a large variety of types have been studied over a period of several years. Most of the strains studied were supplied by Dr. MacDonald Fulton of the Stritch School of Medicine, Loyola University, Chicago, Illinois. Several others came from the Illinois State Health Laboratory, Chicago, and a few from diverse sources.

Flagellar Characteristics

All types of flagellated *Salmonella* appear to have the flagella peritrichously arranged. By far the most common shape of the flagella is normal with wavelengths varying between 2.4 and 2.7 microns (see Table XI). Curly variants are encountered occasionally and appear to be genetic mutants of the normal. In some types such as *Salmonella wichita* the curly variant appears very stable, while in other types such as *Salmonella typhimurium* it appears much less so. Lowering the pH of a suspension does not cause a change from normal to curly as with *Proteus* strains. Other shapes such as coiled and straight have only been observed in odd flagella among otherwise normal types. By careful observation of a large number of organisms a few strains of S. *typhimurium* have shown a rare curly flagellum among the normal flagella and also a rare flagellum partly curly and partly normal (Fig. 47c). One strain of S. *typhimurium,* supplied by the Illinois State Health Laboratory, showed normal flagella but no motion. The paralyzed flagella of this strain were perfectly normal antigenically and developed both antigenic phases (i:1,2,3). The change of antigenic phase in the diphasic types of *Salmonella* does not appear to be associated with any significant change of flagellar wavelength. In Fig. 48 is shown an interesting filamentous form of *Salmonella typhimurium.*

112

TABLE XI
Mean Flagellar Wavelengths of Some Salmonella Species or Types[a]

Species or type	H antigen	Wavelength (microns)	Species or type	H antigen	Wavelength (microns)
schottmuelleri, 8006	b:1,2	2.42	essen	g,m:—	2.58
schottmuelleri, odense	b:1,2	2.45	enteritidis	g,m:—	2.52
schleissheim	b,z_{12}:—	2.49	montevideo, 2	g,m,s:—	2.58
typhosa, T2 (curly)	d:—	1.14	montevideo, 623	g,m,s:—	2.68
typhosa, Watson	d:—	2.42	budapest	g,t:—	2.69
typhosa, H901	d:—	2.42	rostock	g,p,n:—	2.48
typhosa, 2V	d:—	2.55	moscow	g,q:—	2.48
typhosa, R2 (rough)	d:—	2.59	senftenberg	g,s,t:—	2.52
virginia	d:—	2.49	typhimurium, Friever	i:1,2	2.47
wichita (curly)	d:—	1.16	typhimurium, 1406	i:1,2	2.52
wichita (normal)	d:—	2.54	typhimurium, 10953	i:1,2	2.55
abortivoequina, B202	e,n,x:—	2.63	typhimurium, 4066	i:1,2	2.55
abortusbovis, B1960	e,n,x:—	2.71	newport	e,h:1,2	2.52
anatum	e,h:1,6	2.54	thompson, 94369	k:1,5	2.66
derby, 31	f,g:—	2.55	thompson, Berlin	k:1,5	2.67
derby, 15145	f,g:—	2.58	choleraesuis, Kunzendorf	c:1,5	2.68
habana, D4	f,g:—	2.45	bredeney, 414	l,v:1,7	2.70
adelaide	f,g:—	2.47	duesseldorf	z_4,z_{24}:—	2.49
berta	f,g,t:—	2.41	cerro	z_4,z_{23},z_{25}:—	2.36
california	g,m,t:—	2.38	simsbury	z_{27}:—	2.20
blegdam, 22	g,m,q:—	2.33			

[a] In most instances only one strain of a type or species was studied and the significance of the recorded mean wavelength must be evaluated with this in mind. The main purpose of the table is to show the range of wavelengths among Salmonella species or types.

113

Fig. 47. a, b, c. *Salmonella typhimurium*, Friewer. In a is shown the normal and in b the curly type of flagella. The curly flagella of S. *typhimurium* seem to have somewhat limited stability and pure curly cultures have shown a high rate of dissociation to the normal type. In c is shown a rare phenomenon in *Salmonella*: a flagellum with the proximal part curly and the distal part normal.

d. S. *typhosa*, Watson. Normal peritrichous flagella. Variants with curly flagella are also found in this species.

e, f. S. *wichita*, Fulton 3216. In e is shown the normal variant and in f the curly variant. These variants have remained stable for years as laboratory broth cultures. The curly variant is only feebly motile with only wiggling and turning movements.

g. S. *virginia*, Fulton 189. Normal peritrichous flagella on a faintly stained soma.

h. S. *enteritidis*, Fulton. Normal peritrichous flagella.

i. S. *derby*, Fulton. Normal peritrichous flagella.

j, k. S. *anatum*, Fulton. Typical normal (j) and curly (k) variants of this species.

l. S. *arizona*, Fulton. Normal peritrichous flagella.

114

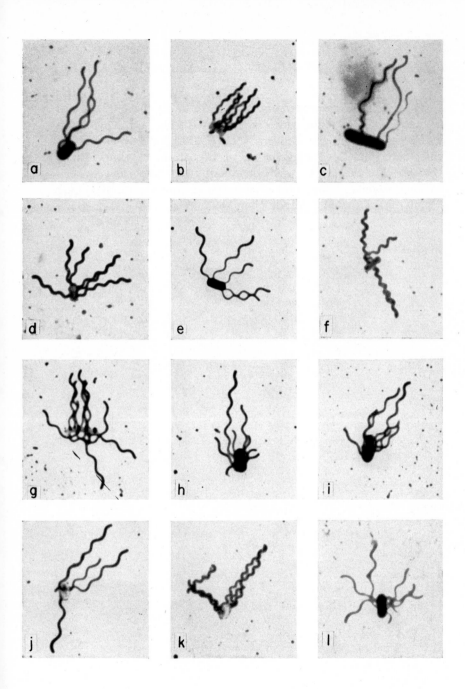

115

46. *Pasteurella*

Pasteurella pseudotuberculosis appears to be the only species in the *Pasteurella* genus which is flagellated (Fig. 49). One strain was received from the University of California School of Medicine, San Francisco. Flagellation of this strain at temperatures between 20° and 30° C. was fair and the organism showed peritrichous flagella of long and very irregular wavelength, averaging 3.2 microns, with an amplitude about 0.8 micron.

FIG. 48. m. S. *typhimurium*, Fulton. A filamentous form with normal peritrichous flagella.

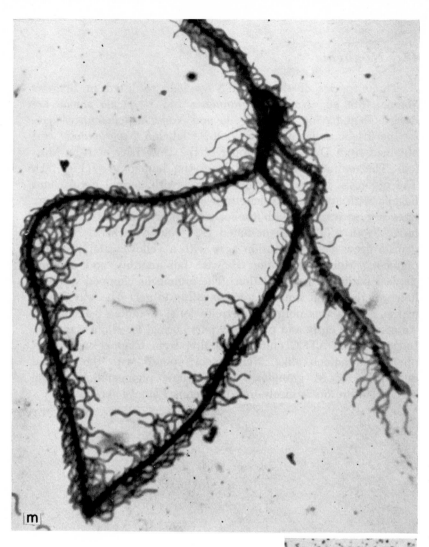

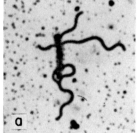

Fig. 49. a. *Pasteurella pseudotuberculosis.* Peritrichous flagella of very irregular wavelength and amplitude.

48. *Photobacterium*

The light producing or luminescent bacteria do not form a homogeneous group either physiologically or morphologically. To group them together into one genus, *Photobacterium*, may not be in the best interest of a sound taxonomy. Luminescence, however, is such a striking phenomenon that one is apt to regard it as of fundamental taxonomic importance even though it is not a particularly stable characteristic.

Five cultures of the group were received from H. Spencer of the Humber Laboratory, England; namely *Photobacterium sepiae*, *P. albensis*, *P. harveyi*, *P. phosphoreum*, and *P. splendidum*. *P. fischeri* was received from M. J. Cormier, Oak Ridge, Tennessee. *P. phosphorescens*, strains L-342 and L-1761, were received from Kluyver's laboratory in Holland through R. S. Breed (see Fig. 51). All the cultures were halophilic and rather psychrophilic. With 3% sodium chloride added to the proper medium and incubated at 20° C., good growth was obtained. With the exception of *P. sepiae*, all produced some light in one medium or another.

FIG. 51. a. *Photobacterium fischeri*, Cormier. Polar multitrichous flagella. The flagella are short with few curves, usually less than one complete wave, and long wavelength. Resembles *Spirillum*.

b. *P. fischeri*, Cormier. Same slide as in a. This picture shows the "microcyst" form which is common in this strain. The flagellation is the same as in the long, or normal, form.

c. *P. phosphorescens*, Kluyver L-342. All individuals in this culture had a spherical soma with a more or less well-defined capsule. Polar monotrichous flagella.

d and e. *P. phosphoreum*, Spencer. All individuals in this culture were spherical with a single flagellum. In e is shown a dividing form with the typical location of the flagellum, indicating polarity.

f. *P. albensis*, Spencer. In addition to the curved rod illustrated, this culture also showed straight rods and spiral forms. The straight and curved rods showed polar monotrichous flagellation. The spiral forms occasionally had tufts of polar flagella.

g, h. *P. splendidum*, Spencer. Both spiral and spherical individuals were present in this culture. In g is shown a slightly spiral form and in h, a spherical form. The flagellation is polar monotrichous.

i. *P. sepiae*, Spencer. Straight rods with polar monotrichous flagella.

j. *P. harveyi*, Spencer. Straight rods with single polar flagella.

120

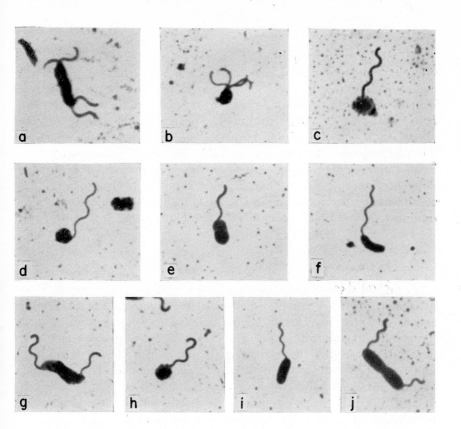

Taxonomy

All strains of light producing bacteria appear to be carbohydrate fermenters and polar flagellated. They could thus be classified either in the genus *Vibrio* or *Aeromonas*. On the bases of somatic morphology and sensitivity to a vibrio static substance (2,4-diamino-6,7-diisopropylpteridine), Spencer would classify *P. sepiae* and *P. harveyi* in the *Aeromonas* genus and the others in the *Vibrio* genus. As recorded in Table XII the flagellar wavelengths of *P. harveyi* and *P. sepiae* are much alike and distinctly different from the others, which lends support to the Spencer classification. The flagellation of *P. fischeri*, however, is different from any typical *Vibrio* species and more like spirilla.

Flagellar Characteristics

P. fischeri showed polar multitrichous flagellation. The flagella were short, with few curves, usually less than one complete wave, and of very long wavelength. Some individuals were short spiral forms, others practically spherical. The somatic morphology and flagellation resemble the marine spirilla in which the spherical form, or microcyst, is quite usual. *P. phosphoreum*, both the Spencer strain and the two Kluyver strains, showed a spherical soma and a single flagellum of somewhat longer than the average wavelength of most polar monotrichous bacteria. By observing the location of the flagellum in dividing forms it was evident that the flagellum had a polar location. *P. albensis* showed a variety of somatic types—small straight rods, small curved rods, and long spiral filaments. On the small forms the flagellation was polar monotrichous with about 50% of the organisms being amphitrichous. The long spiral forms frequently showed tufts of flagella characteristic of spirilla. *P. harveyi* was a large straight rod with polar monotrichous flagella. The size of the soma and the curvature of the flagella showed great variation. *P. sepiae* showed only straight rods with polar monotrichous flagella. The flagellar wavelength was rather variable and may be of two types. *P. splendidum* showed a very pleomorphic soma with spherical forms, straight and slightly curved rods, and definitely spiral forms. The flagellation was polar monotrichous without the flagellar tufts seen in *P. albensis*. None of the cultures examined showed any very definite flagellar variants.

122

TABLE XII
MORPHOLOGICAL CHARACTERISTICS OF LUMINESCENT BACTERIA

Species	Soma	Flagella		Genus proposed by Spencer
		Arrangement	Wavelength (microns)	
P. fischeri	Curved and oval	Polar multitrichous	3.1	Vibrio
P. phosphoreum (Spencer)	Spherical	Polar monotrichous	3.1	Vibrio
P. phosphoreum (Kluyver)	Spherical	Polar monotrichous	2.4	Vibrio
P. albensis	Curved	Polar monotrichous and multitrichous	2.3	Vibrio
P. splendidum	Curved and oval	Polar monotrichous	2.1	Vibrio
P. harveyi	Straight rod	Polar monotrichous	1.5	Aeromonas
P. sepiae	Straight rod	Polar monotrichous	1.5	Aeromonas

49. Bacillus

Thirty-eight cultures, representing twenty-one species, of the genus *Bacillus* were studied morphologically. The identity of the cultures was accepted as labeled by the donors. The majority of the cultures were from the R. N. Smith Collection and were received from William B. Haynes of the Northern Regional Research Laboratory, Peoria, Illinois. Several cultures were from Kenneth Burdon, University of Texas. With the exception of *Bacillus pasteurii*, which required addition of 1% urea to the medium, all cultures grew readily in simple peptone broth. Only one thermophile, *Bacillus stearothermophilus*, was studied and this was incubated at 55° C.

FIG. 52. a. *Bacillus subtilis*, NRRL B-642. Typical normal and coiled flagella.

b. *B. subtilis*, NRRL B-642. This is a somewhat unusual organism for this species, showing two normal and two curly flagella.

c. *B. pumilus*, Burdon Ba 7(5). Normal and coiled flagella.

d. *B. megaterium*, NRRL B-349. Normal flagella. This strain also showed some coiled flagella.

e. *B. cereus*, Burden Ba 2(7). Normal flagella. Flagella of two distinctly different wavelengths were observed in this culture. The shorter wavelength flagella had a wavelength about 1.6 microns which is greater than typical curly flagella.

f, g. *B. macerans*, NRS 1093. In f is shown the normal and in g the curly variant of this strain.

h. *B. macerans*, NRRL B-171. This strain had a unique flagellation. The flagella are short, stiff, and with a very short wavelength—compare with g.

i. *B. macerans*, NRRL B-172. Still a different picture of *B. macerans* showing lightly stained soma with normal flagella on one individual and curly flagella on the other. The normal flagella have a shorter wavelength than those of strain 1093 shown in f.

j. *B. polymyxa*, NRRL B-173. Normal flagella of somewhat irregular curvature.

124

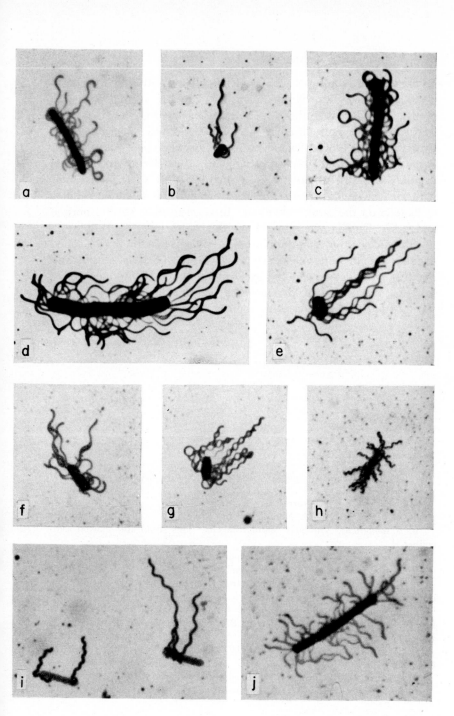

125

Some of the cultures were well flagellated, others very poorly flagellated (see Figs. 52 and 53). The flagellar arrangement was peritrichous in all cultures. Three types of flagellar curvature were observed: normal, curly, and coiled. A few species showed normal flagella only. Some strains of *Bacillus macerans* and of *B. pasteurii* showed only curly flagella, other strains only normal flagella, and still other strains a mixture with some individuals with curly flagella, some with normal flagella, but not both kinds of flagella on the same individual. In several other species normal and curly flagella were found on the same individual. Also in several species the same individual might show normal and coiled flagella, and even normal, curly, and coiled. *Bacillus subtilis* and *Bacillus pumilus* showed the greatest tendency to produce coiled flagella. One strain of *B. macerans* was quite unique with only short, stiff curly flagella with shorter wavelength than the curly

---

FIG. 53. k. *Bacillus circulans*, NRRL B-378. Normal flagella of rather short wavelength.

l. *B. alvei*, NRS-811. Normal flagella.

m. *B. brevis*, NRS-1138. Normal flagella.

n. *B. sphaericus*, NRS-348. Normal flagella. This strain also showed some coiling.

o. *B. pasteurii*, NRS-673. Normal flagella.

p. *B. pasteurii*, NRS-674. Curly flagella.

q. *Bacillus* sp., A-J. This picture is from a culture labeled bacillus A-J, received from Dr. Eleanor Alexander-Jackson. It is claimed by the donor to cause human cancer and was isolated from human cancerous tissue. The flagellar morphology is very similar to *B. cereus* with flagella of two distinct wavelengths.

r. *B. stearothermophilus*, NRRL B-1172. Normal flagella. This was the only thermophile studied.

s. *B. lentus*, NRRL B-396. Normal and coiled flagella.

t. *B. coagulans*, NRRL B-1167. Normal flagella.

126

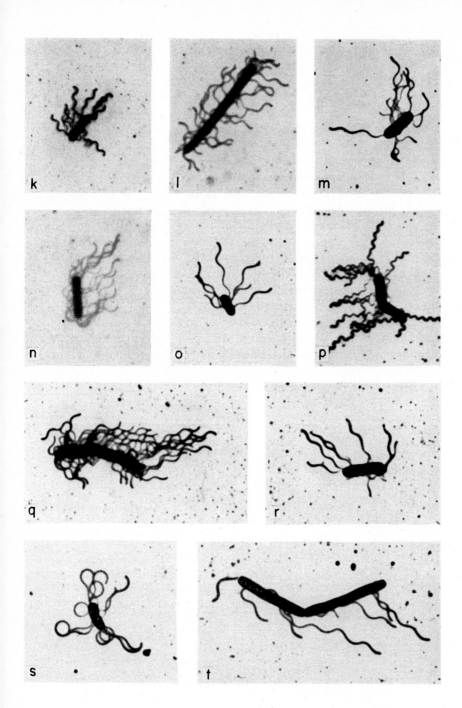

127

flagella of the other strains and species. Considerable variation was found in the wavelengths of the normal flagella of the different species (see Table XIII). The shortest normal wavelengths were found in *Bacillus circulans* and the longest in *Bacillus megatherium*.

Bacillus sphaericus showed pH sensitive flagella. When stained from a 1% dibasic potassium phosphate suspension the flagella were all of normal curvature, but from a monobasic potassium phosphate suspension they were mainly curly.

Bacillus cereus and the Alexander-Jackson (A-J) strain showed mainly normal flagella but mixed with the normal were some flagella with shorter wavelength but not sufficiently short to be labeled curly. The wavelength of these flagella averaged 1.6 microns in *B. cereus* and 1.5 microns in the A-J strain. The difference between these wavelengths and wavelengths of true curly flagella (1.1–1.25 microns) is readily apparent by direct observation.

The flagellar wavelengths may be of considerable value in the speciation of the genus *Bacillus*. However, to have any great significance, many more strains must be studied than the author has done to date.

TABLE XIII
Mean Flagellar Wavelengths of *Bacillus* Species

Species	Strains	Wavelength (microns)		Species	Strains	Wavelength (microns)	
		Normal	Curly			Normal	Curly
B. pasteurii	4	—	1.17	*B. sphaericus*	3	2.7	1.12
B. circulans	3	1.8	—	*B. firmus*	1	2.7	—
B. macerans 171	1	—	1.02	*B. technicus*	1	2.7	1.22
B. macerans 1096	1	1.9	—	*B. pumilus*	3	2.9	1.12
B. macerans 172	1	2.0	1.10	*B. lentus*	1	2.9	—
B. macerans 1097	1	2.3	1.21	*B. polymyxa*	1	3.0	1.12
B. macerans 1093, 1095	2	2.6	1.26	*B. pantothenicus*	1	3.0	—
B. pulvifaciens	1	2.2	—	*B. coagulans*	1	3.3	—
B. subtilis	3	2.3–2.5	1.10	*B. megaterium*	1	3.9	—
B. licheniformis	3	2.2–2.6	1.15	*B. cereus*	3	2.4–2.8	1.62[a]
B. brevis	1	2.5	1.18	*Bacillus* sp., A-J	1	2.5	1.50[a]
B. stearothermophilus	1	2.3–2.6	1.25				
B. laterosporus	1	2.6	—				
B. alvei	1	2.6	—				

[a] These are not typical curly types.

50. *Clostridium*

Thirty-one species of *Clostridium* were studied with two or more strains of each species. The cultures were supplied by Dr. L. S. McClung of Indiana University. In agreement with the literature the only definitely nonflagellated and nonmotile species was *Clostridium perfringens,* of which five strains were studied. The single strain of *Clostridium nigrificans* studied did not show any flagella but the growth was not entirely satisfactory and much significance should not be attached to this finding.

FLAGELLAR CHARACTERISTICS

All the motile strains studied showed peritrichous flagellation. With a few exceptions the flagella stained readily. Some species of *Clostridium* grow with difficulty in media without particulate matter and had to be cultured in thioglycollate medium (0.1% agar), corn mash, etc., which made washing not entirely satisfactory. The flagella of three species stained with more difficulty than those of the other species. These were *Clostridium felsineum, C. acetobutylicum,* and *C. roseum. C. acetobutylicum* and *C. roseum* are very similar morphologically. Strain McClung 638 of *C. felsineum* showed normal flagella only but strain 639 showed flagella much like *C. acetobutylicum* with a mixture of flagella of short and long wavelength. This species requires further study but morphologically it appears very similar to *C. acetobutylicum* and *C. roseum.* The flagellation of *Clostridium tetani* deserves special mention. Two strains were studied and, while one was better flagellated than the other, both showed the same type of flagella which were rather stiff with relatively short wavelength and large amplitude. The same type of flagella, with longer wavelength, was also found in the strains of *Clostridium novyi* studied. This flagellation, if similar in all strains, is so distinctive as to be diagnostic.

In some species of *Clostridium* only normal flagella were observed, in other species the flagellation was predominantly normal with an occasional curly flagellum mixed in with the normal. Several species showed both normal and curly flagellated individuals. Coiled flagella were particularly prominent in the acetobutylicum group. Straight flagella were observed only in *Clostridium aerofoetidum*, McClung 1148, which showed a few individuals with straight flagella. Several flagellar variants were observed in *Clostridium tetanomorphum* as illustrated (Figs. 54, 55, and 56).

Fɪɢ. 54. a. *Clostridium difficile,* McClung 871. The three strains studied showed an identical picture. Note the exceptionally short wavelength, shorter than that of curly flagella on most bacteria.

b. *C. tetani,* McClung 148. Two strains studied showed practically an identical picture. The slides showed only normal flagella with the shortest normal wavelength of all clostridia studied, excepting *C. difficile* which may have been curly variants. The flagella of *C. tetani* appear to be very stiff with relatively large amplitude. They are very characteristic and practically diagnostic.

c. *C. capitovale,* McClung 1237. The two strains studied were identical and showed normal flagella only. The flagellar wavelength is relatively short and amplitude relatively great. Flagella give impression of being rather delicate.

d. *C. novyi,* McClung 151. Normal peritrichous flagella of rather large amplitude. The flagellation resembles that of *C. tetani* except for greater wavelength. A few curly types seen.

e. *C. botulinum,* McClung 662. Normal flagella. Two of the three strains studied were atrichous. The strain pictured showed a few partly curly flagella.

f. *C. septicum,* McClung 1019. This is a medium length filament, many were several times this length, and characteristic of *C. septicum.* The flagella pictured are of normal type with rather short wavelength and small amplitude. In organisms other than that pictured curly flagella were interspersed among the normal.

g. *C. felsineum,* McClung 638. The organism pictured is typical of strain 638, with normal flagella which stained readily. However, strain 639 showed more a picture resembling *C. acetobutylicum* and the flagella were difficult to stain. Further study is necessary to definitely elucidate the flagellar characteristics of this species.

h. *C. chauvoei* (*feseri*), McClung 1436. Normal flagella. No variants observed.

i. *C. centrosporogenes,* McClung 136. Normal flagella. With the exception of a single curly flagellum all flagella seen in this culture were normal.

j. *C. bifermentans,* McClung 435. Only normal flagella observed on both strains studied.

k. *C. lentoputrescens,* McClung 998. Normal flagella. The one strain studied showed excellent flagellation with all flagella of normal curvature.

132

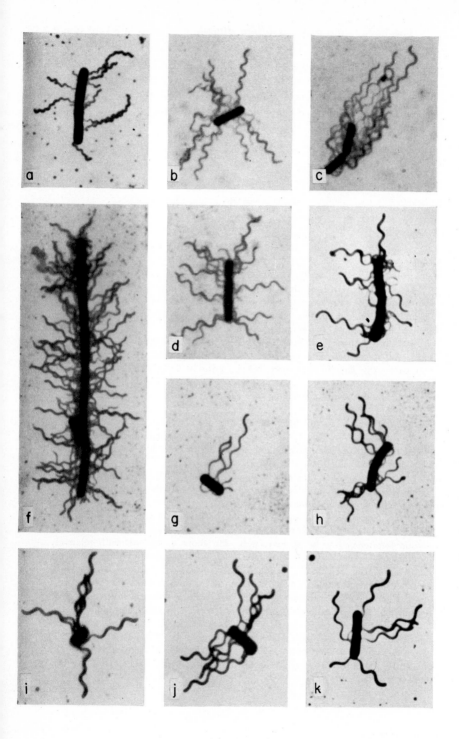

The flagellation of *Clostridium difficile* was most unusual if not unique for the genus *Clostridium*. Three strains of this species were studied (McClung 870, 871, 1253) and all three were identical. The wavelength of the flagella is shorter than that of curly flagella in general and sufficiently distinctive to be diagnostic. Flagella of more normal wavelength were not found in this species (see Table XIV).

FIG. 55. l, m, n. *Clostridium aerofoetidum*, McClung 1148. In addition to individuals with pure normal and pure curly flagella a few individuals were found with straight flagella. This is the only *Clostridium* species in which straight flagella have been observed.

o. *C. histolyticum*, McClung 1292. Two strains were studied both of which were well flagellated with predominantly normal flagella. A few part normal and part curly flagella were seen but no entirely curly flagella nor curly individuals.

p. *C. parabotulinum*, McClung 489. Typical normal flagella of this species. Twenty-one strains were studied and only in two was a very rare curly or partly curly flagellum seen. Most strains were well flagellated.

q. *C. carnis*, McClung 1249. Two strains were studied. Both showed good flagellation with flagella predominantly normal with a few curly flagella on some individuals along with the normal types.

r. *C. thermosaccharolyticum*, McClung 919-A. The flagellation of this strain was very poor and the organism pictured was the best that could be found. The flagella had normal curvature.

s. *C. sphenoides*, McClung 1183. The flagellation of this organism is very similar to that of *C. butyricum*. The flagella on the one strain studied were all normal but seemed to be of two kinds. On those individuals with relatively long flagella the wavelength averaged 2.67 microns, and on those with the relatively shorter flagella the wavelength averaged 3.12 microns. The possible presence of two variants must be determined by further study.

t. *C. cochlearium*, McClung 257. This culture showed practically pure normal flagella. A rare curly flagellum was seen with small amplitude.

u. *C. butyricum*, McClung 629. The flagella are peritrichous and of normal, rather long, wavelength. The flagella tend to be rather short.

v. *C. butylicum*, McClung 1670. Normal flagella of somewhat irregular curvature. About 20% of the individuals showed curly flagella and the rest normal flagella.

134

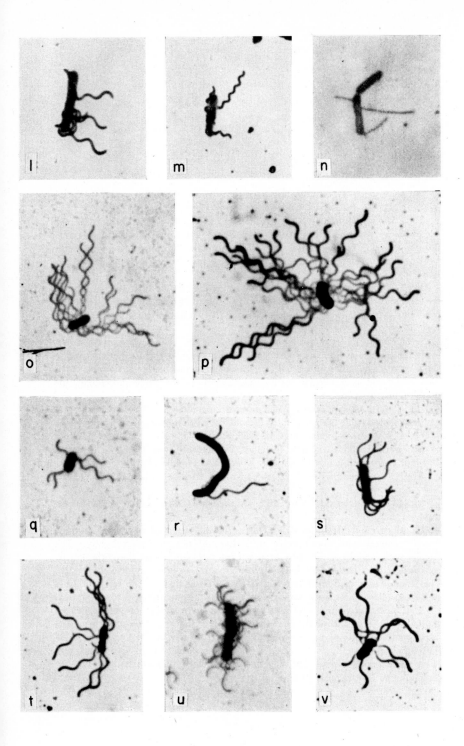

FIG. 56. w. *Clostridium* sp. 3679, McClung 174. Three strains of this organism were studied. With the exception of a few partly curly and partly normal flagella the flagellation was pure normal. This organism has highly heat-resistant spores and is used in the canning industry as a check on sterilization.

x, y. *C. sporogenes,* McClung 175. In x are shown the typical normal flagella and in y the curly flagella. Of seven strains studied three were pure curly types. In *C. sporogenes* the curly variant apparently is a stable type.

z, aa, bb, cc. *C. tetanomorphum,* McClung 2038. The culture stained was fairly far advanced into the spore stage and a younger culture perhaps would show more flagella per individual. Pictured are several variants; normal, curly, part curly and part normal, curly and normal on the same individual, and double curvature.

dd. *C. tertium,* McClung 1272. Two strains were studied and both were well flagellated with predominantly normal flagella and some coiling tendency.

ee. *C. aurantibutyricum,* McClung 2038. The organism pictured has four or five normal and two curly flagella. The culture was about half normal and half curly with a few individuals with mixed flagella like the one pictured.

ff. *C. pasteurianum,* McClung 308. Normal flagella with long wavelength. No variants seen.

gg. *C. beijerinckii,* McClung 1673. Normal but rather short flagella of long wavelength.

hh. *C. roseum,* McClung 653. This organism was well flagellated but the flagella stained with considerable difficulty and always rather lightly. The flagella were mainly of the curly type but interspersed among the curly flagella were often flagella of very long wavelength and usually also coiled flagella. The resemblance to *C. acetobutylicum* is so striking that a close relationship is suggested. Best stains were obtained by doubling the tannic acid concentration.

ii. *C. acetobutylicum,* McClung 633. The two strains of this organism studied showed beautiful flagellation with a flagellar density equal to or surpassing such organisms as *Proteus.* The great majority of the flagella were of the curly type, usually interspersed with flagella of very long wavelength and often some coiled types. The flagella stained with some difficulty. The resemblance to *C. roseum* is striking.

136

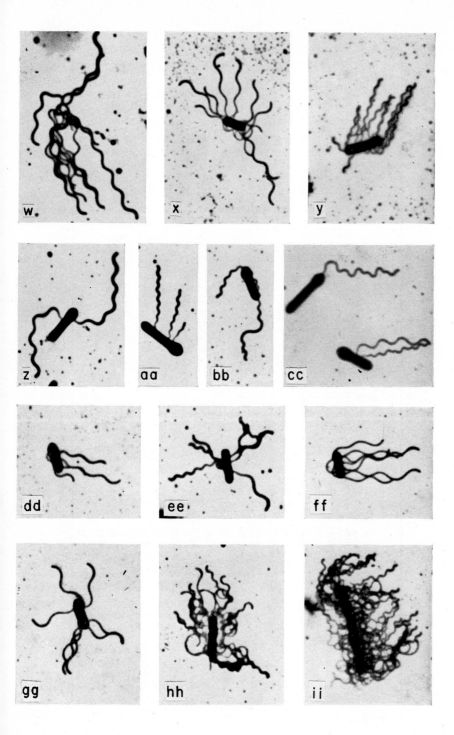

TABLE XIV
Flagellar Wavelengths of Clostridium Species

Species	Strain	Wavelength (microns)		Species average (normal)
		Normal	Curly	
C. difficile	870	0.86	—	
	871	0.86	—	
	1253	0.86	—	0.86
C. tetani	148	1.75	—	
	442	1.80	—	1.77
C. capitovale	1237	1.89	—	
	1238	1.80	—	1.85
C. septicum	1019	1.86	—	
	1020	1.86	—	1.86
C. botulinum	C-662	2.06	—	2.06
C. novyi	26	2.31	—	
	151[a]	2.10	—	2.20
C. felsineum	638	2.24	—	
	639	2.24	1.20	2.24
C. chauvei	1436	2.33	—	
	1655	2.28	—	2.30
C. centrosporogenes	136	2.35	—	2.35

Species	Strain	Wavelength (microns)		Species average (normal)
		Normal	Curly	
C. parabotulinum (continued)	467	2.43	—	
	468	2.53	—	
	472	2.50	—	
	474	2.42	—	
	475	2.48	—	
	480	2.51	—	
	488	2.49	—	
	510	2.50	—	
	514	2.46	—	2.49
C. thermosaccharolyticum	919A	2.60	—	2.60
C. sphenoides	1183	2.67	(3.52)	2.67
C. butyricum	629	2.70	1.16	2.70
C. cochlearium	257	2.73	—	2.73
Clostridium sp. 3679	174	2.93	—	
	222	2.70	—	
	1043	2.80	—	2.81
C. sporogenes	175	2.92	—	

[a] This strain was poorly flagellated but appeared different from strain 26 which was well flagellated.

TABLE XIV (continued)

Species	Strain	Wavelength (microns) Normal	Wavelength (microns) Curly	Species average (normal)
C. bifermentans	135	2.36	—	
	435	2.40	—	2.38
C. lentoputrescens	998	2.38	—	2.38
C. histolyticum	1286	2.37	—	
	1292	2.39	1.09	2.38
C. aerofoetidum	1148	2.44	1.14	2.44
C. carnis	1248	2.49	—	
	1249	2.47	—	2.48
C. parabotulinum	446	2.46	—	
	447	2.52	—	
	450	2.42	—	
	453	2.62	—	
	455	2.55	—	
	456	2.48	—	
	458	2.48	—	
	460	2.58	—	
	462	2.53	—	

Species	Strain	Wavelength (microns) Normal	Wavelength (microns) Curly	Species average (normal)
	177	2.90	—	
	418	3.05	—	
	916	2.96	—	2.95
	213	—	1.20	
	225	—	1.14	
	269	—	1.30	
C. tetanomorphum	1240	2.95	1.14	2.95
C. butylicum	1670	2.98	1.18	2.98
C. aurantibutyricum	2038	2.98	1.24	2.98
C. tertium	1263	3.09	—	
	1272	2.98	—	3.04
C. pasteurianum	308	3.46	—	3.46
C. roseum	653	2.6	(3.2) 1.15	2.6
C. acetobutylicum	632	—	1.17	
	633	2.71	(4.27)	2.71
C. beijerinckii	1671	3.86	—	3.86

51. Caulobacter

In Bergey's Manual is listed only one species of *Caulobacter*, *Caulobacter vibrioides*. This organism is one of the most common bacteria in natural waters. It is present in the distilled water of the author's laboratory at all times. When bacterial cultures are washed for flagella staining a few caulobacter may invariably be found on the slides and may be mistaken for a variant of the cul-

---

Fig. 57. a. *Caulobacter vibrioides*. A typical individual organism showing a single polar flagellum of very short wavelength.

b. *C. vibrioides*. This picture shows an individual with a stalk and a flagellum at the end of the stalk.

c, d, e. *C. vibrioides*. Here are shown various degrees of rosette formation. The individuals appear to be attached to each other. Flagella develop on the daughter cells when division is about complete.

f. *C. vibrioides* attached by a stalk to a staphylococcus. The *Caulobacter* flagellum is still attached to the end of the stalk.

g, h. *C. vibrioides* attached to an unidentified water organism with a single polar flagellum. Note the difference in wavelength of the flagella of the unidentified organism and *Caulobacter*.

i. *C. vibrioides* attached to *Salmonella wichita*. There are several salmonella in the clump and the flagella with the longer wavelength are salmonella flagella. The smaller organisms around the periphery are *Caulobacter* and two of these at the bottom of the picture show flagella.

j. *C. vibrioides* attached to *Sarcina ureae*. The rounded curves of several sarcinae may be seen along the upper right edge of the dense mass. Several sarcinae flagella of long wavelength emerge from the upper part of the clump and one from the lower part. Many caulobacter flagella are evident.

k. *C. vibrioides*. The three pictures show the morphology of caulobacter in slightly alkaline media of pH 7.5 to 8.0; pH 8.0 was the upper limit for growth. In the somewhat alkaline medium caulobacter grew very poorly and produced few stalks and few flagella. Note the strongly curved soma. The organism shown in the upper right was very exceptional in having both a stalk and a flagellum.

l. *C. vibrioides*. In media with osmotic pressure equivalent to about 1% sodium chloride and at a pH not lower than 6.5, caulobacter grows slowly and in the form of long and somewhat curved filaments. The filament may have a single polar flagellum as illustrated, one or more lateral flagella or, most frequently, no flagella.

m. *C. vibrioides* from a mixed culture with *Bacillus pumilis*. This is a rather unusual involution form.

n. *C. vibrioides* rosette from which has grown out a long filament. This picture is from a normal culture in which filaments are extremely rare. Note the flagellum at the end of the filament.

140

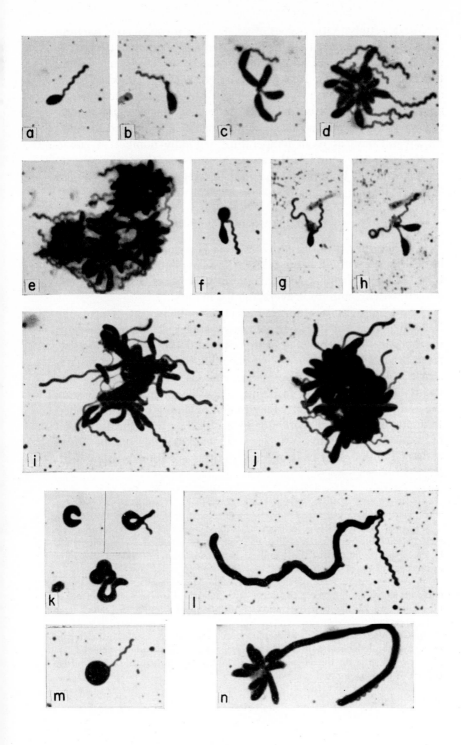

ture under study. Other types of small polar monotrichous bacteria may also be found in the distilled water and consequently on the flagella slides. If confusion is likely, the water used for washing the bacteria must be freshly distilled or freshly boiled. In the author's experience the *Caulobacter* in distilled water usually have no flagella but do have a long stalk which makes them readily recognized. If a washed suspension of bacteria is allowed to stand for several days at room temperature a goodly number of caulobacter is usually found in the suspension, where they may or may not be attached by stalks to the washed bacteria (see Figs. 57 and 58).

Flagellar Characteristics

C. vibrioides in the free living state is a small rod which may be straight, or curved like a vibrio. The flagellation is polar monotrichous. The flagellar wavelength is very short, averaging 0.95 micron with an amplitude averaging 0.4 micron.

In all the cultures studied, for causes unknown at present, the individual bacteria soon begin to grow stalks. The stalk develops on the flagellated end of the organism and the flagellum persists for a limited time on the end of the stalk, even when the stalk is attached to some particulate matter, such as other bacteria. When the stalked bacteria start to divide a new flagellum develops from the end distal to the stalk. Many individuals may become attached to a single particle of matter or to each other with the formation of small and large rosettes. New flagella develop on the distal ends of the daughter cells and the rosettes are soon bristling with flagella.

Fig. 58. o. This picture is from a distilled water suspension of *Bacillus megaterium* and caulobacter. The caulobacter is attached by a long stalk to the upper right end of the bacillus. Note the short caulobacter flagellum at the base of the stalk.

p. An involution form of caulobacter with two polar flagella and apparently attached to a *Listeria* organism with straight flagella. This is from a mixed culture of the two organisms. Multiple polar flagella on caulobacter were very rare.

q. *Caulobacter* attached to staphylococci and to each other. From the masses of staphylococci and caulobacter emerge long filaments of caulobacter. Note two flagella on the filament at the right. This picture is from a mixed culture of caulobacter and staphylococci.

142

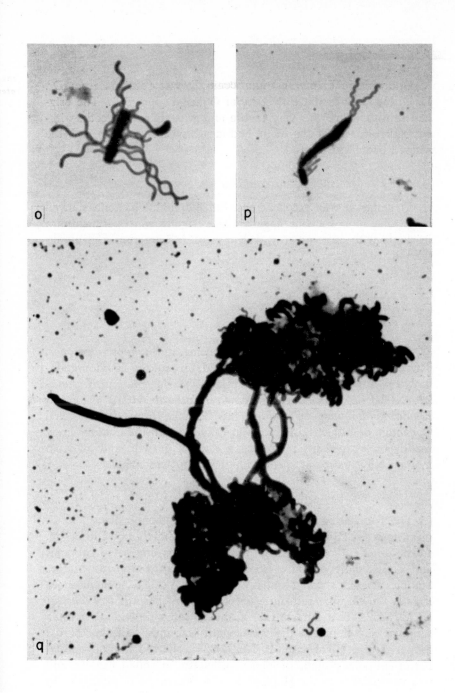

143

52. *Chromatium*

One culture of *Chromatium* strain D was received from Dr. D. D. Hendley of the University of Chicago (Fig. 59). The original broth culture was very motile and was stained directly without subculture. The growth had a distinct red color and the massed bacteria were red.

FLAGELLAR CHARACTERISTICS

Flagellation was excellent and the individual bacteria showed long polar monotrichous flagella. The flagella were very uniform in shape with an average wavelength of 2.05 microns and amplitude of 0.47 micron.

53. *Rhodopseudomonas*

The Bergey's Manual lists four species of *Rhodopseudomonas*. Three of these species were obtained for study: *Rhodopseudomonas palustris* ATH 2.1.1 from Hopkins Marine Station; *R. palustris*, NCIB 8252; *Rhodopseudomonas gelatinosa*, NCIB 8290; and *Rhodopseudomonas spheroides*, NCIB 8253, from the National Collection of Industrial Bacteria in England. All the cultures grew readily on agar slants producing a reddish growth, and all were motile. No attempt at species identification was made.

FLAGELLAR CHARACTERISTICS

The flagellation of the four cultures was monotrichous. In *R. gelatinosa*, NCIB 8290, the flagellum was definitely polar in origin. In the other three cultures the flagellum often originated subpolar and occasionally actually lateral. *R. palustris*, Hopkins Marine Station strain, showed mainly subpolar, coiled monotrichous flagella which appeared quite different from those of *R. palustris*, NCIB 8252. This latter strain also had some individuals with a subpolar flagellum but the wavelength was only half that of the former strain. *R. spheroides*, NCIB 8253, showed a goodly number of subpolar flagella of long wavelength, or coiled flagella, and was very similar to the Hopkins Marine Station of *R. palustris*. In this strain the flagellum was often lateral. (See Fig. 60.)

144

Fig. 59. a. *Chromatium* sp., Hendley-Gaffron Strain D. Polar monotrichous flagella.

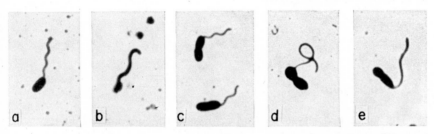

Fig. 60. a. *Rhodopseudomonas palustris,* NCIB 8252. Polar monotrichous flagella. Some individuals of this strain had a subpolar flagellum. Mean flagellar wavelength 1.58 microns.

b. *R. palustris,* Hopkins Marine Station 2.1.1. This culture was very poorly flagellated. Most flagellated individuals showed subpolar monotrichous coiled flagella. The soma stained very lightly. Flagellar wavelength from 3 to 4 microns.

c. *R. gelatinosa,* NCIB 8290. Polar monotrichous flagella of normal curvature. This strain showed only polar flagella. Mean flagellar wavelength 1.63 microns.

d, e. *R. spheroides,* NCIB 8253. Note the long wavelength of the flagella and the lateral origin in d. Individuals with subpolar and lateral flagella were as frequent in this strain as those with polar flagella. Flagellar wavelength was 3 to 4 microns.

145

54. *Rhodospirillum*

Two species of *Rhodospirillum* are listed in Bergey's Manual, *Rhodospirillum rubrum* and *Rhodospirillum fulvum*. Several strains of *R. rubrum* were obtained for study from several sources. *R. fulvum* was not obtained.

FLAGELLAR CHARACTERISTICS

R. rubrum is a typical spirillum with a tuft of polar flagella at one or both ends. The flagella rarely have more than one curve as in most spirilla (Fig. 61).

55. *Nocardia*

The great majority of *Nocardia* organisms encountered in nature appear to be nonmotile and presumably nonflagellated. A culture labeled *Nocardia*, Örskov, was received from Mortimer P. Starr of the University of California (Fig. 62). This strain originated from Dr. J. Örskov in Denmark. The culture showed mainly relatively small pleomorphic rods with a few short filaments. Motility was fair.

FLAGELLAR CHARACTERISTICS

The majority of individuals showed only one flagellum or none. A fair number showed two flagella and a few showed many flagella. The flagella were very irregular as to length and curvature. Some were almost straight, others coiled, and some showed uneven waves. The arrangement of the flagella was distinctly nonpolar or peritrichous. The wavelength of the wavy flagella was very great but so uneven that an average wavelength has little significance. The most distinct waves measured around 5 microns in length.

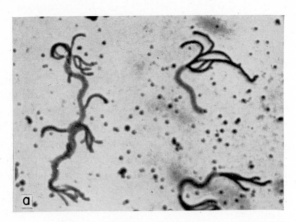

Fig. 61. a. *Rhodospirillum rubrum,* Hopkins Marine Station ATR 1.1.1. Tufts of flagella at one or both poles. Flagella rarely have more than one curve. From E. Leifson, *J. Bacteriol.* **62**, 377-389 (1951).

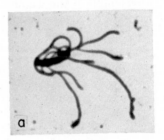

Fig. 62. a. *Nocardia* sp., Örskov. Peritrichous flagella with irregular waves. Most flagellated individuals in the culture had only one or two flagella.

147

56. *Borrelia*

Two types of *Borrelia* were studied, neither in artificial culture. The one organism, *Borrelia novyi*, was stained directly from the blood of an infected mouse. The blood was carefully collected into citrated saline solution, the blood cells removed by slow centrifugation, and the spirochetes washed in the usual manner. The other organism studied came from the mouth of a human male with Vincent's angina. This organism may be labeled *Borrelia vincentii* (Fig. 63).

FLAGELLAR CHARACTERISTICS

B. novyi was actively motile and flagella stain showed numerous peritrichous flagella of normal curvature. No variants were observed. The average wavelength was 1.9 microns. *B. vincentii* showed numerous flagella with peritrichous arrangement and normal curvature. No distinct variants were observed. The average wavelength of the flagella was 2.0 microns.

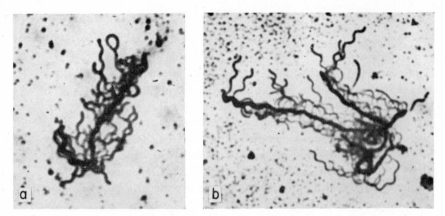

FIG. 63. a. *Borrelia novyi*. Peritrichous flagella of normal curvature. Stained directly from mouse blood.

b. *B. vincentii*. Peritrichous flagella of normal curvature. Stained directly from material from the human mouth.

a. From E. Leifson, *J. Bacteriol.* **60**, 678-679 (1950).

57. *Treponema*

Several unsuccessful attempts were made to secure material for direct study of *Treponema pallidum* from syphilitic chancres. The number of spirochetes were too few and got lost in the wash. Attempts at direct staining of spirochetes from infected rabbit testicle were also unsuccessful. Several strains of cultivated *Treponema* were stained and some of these are illustrated. Included among these were strains labeled *T. pallidum,* Reiter, Nichol, Kazan, and Noguchi. Some oral strains of *Treponema* were also studied.

FLAGELLAR CHARACTERISTICS

The Reiter strains of *T. pallidum* showed the best and most unequivocal flagellation. The flagellation was subpolar multitrichous as illustrated in Figs. 64c and d. This appears to be the basic flagellation of *Treponema*. The Kazan strain of *T. pallidum* also showed this type of flagellation on some individuals. Many individuals of the strains named, and also the Nichol and Noguchi strains, showed subpolar monotrichous flagellation. This type is probably the same as subpolar multitrichous.

Many individuals in most strains showed a polar monotrichous flagellum-like structure illustrated in Fig. 64a. If this had been the only flagellum-like structure seen in *Treponema* it would certainly have been labeled a polar flagellum. In the literature it is referred to as a polar filament. A similar type of filament sometimes may be seen connecting two organisms as in Fig. 64b. These polar and intersomal filaments have about the same wavelength as the soma. So, for that matter, also have the subpolar flagella. The average wavelength of the subpolar flagella is 1.2 microns.

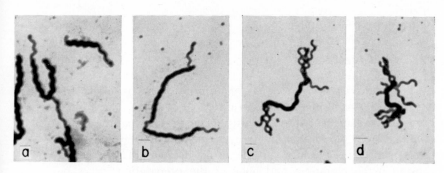

Fig. 64. a. *Treponema pallidum*, Reiter strain. The polar structures on these spirochetes are commonly referred to as terminal filaments and may not be flagella.

b. *Treponema* sp., Oral type, Hampp. The upper organism has a single subpolar flagellum. Connecting the two organisms is a filament probably of the same nature as the terminal filament on the lower organism.

c, d. *T. pallidum*, Reiter strain. Characteristic subpolar multitrichous flagellation. In c is shown this type of flagellation particularly well.

a–d. From E. Leifson, *J. Bacteriol.* **62**, 377-389 (1951).

58. Bartonella

Two cultures of *Bartonella bacilliformis* were received from Aristidis Herrer, Lima, Peru. Transfers to various blood media grew the organisms rather scantily. The best preparations were obtained from blood agar slants by suspending the growth in distilled water and washing in the usual manner. The organisms showed much clumping and none of the preparations were particularly good.

FLAGELLAR CHARACTERISTICS

In spite of the frequent location of the flagella at the poles of the soma the organism appears definitely to be peritrichous. The flagellation was poor, the organisms usually in clumps, which left few isolated, flagellated individuals on the slides. The flagellar wavelength was very short, averaging 0.95 micron with an average amplitude of 0.25 micron (Fig. 65).

152

Fig. 65. a. *Bartonella bacilliformis,* Herrer VS 306. The picture shows what appears to be two individuals more or less end to end. Although the flagella are somewhat concentrated at the poles they are definitely peritrichous in arrangement. Note the tiny wavelength.

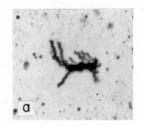

59. *Selenomonas*

The genus *Selenomonas* apparently has a ubiquitous distribution in nature. It appears to be a common inhabitant of the cow rumen, the human throat, dog intestine, river water, etc. It is anaerobic and somewhat fastidious in its growth requirements. Morphologically it is unique, with a slight curvature to the soma and unusual flagellar arrangement (Fig. 66).

One culture labeled *Selenomonas ruminantium* was received from Marvin Bryant of the U.S.D.A. It was isolated from cow rumen. Similar appearing organisms were seen by the author in material from dog intestine and in river water but these were not isolated. A culture labeled *Spirillum sputigenum* was received from J. B. Macdonald of Harvard University. Growth of this organism was rather unsatisfactory but sufficient organisms were present for staining.

Fig. 66. a, b, c. *Selenomonas ruminantium,* Bryant. These are typical examples of single individuals. The soma is slightly curved and the flagella originate as a tuft from the concave side.

d, e. *S. ruminantium,* Bryant. These organisms appear to be in the process of cell division. In d the left half is starting to develop flagella. In e each half has a distinct tuft of flagella.

f. *S. ruminantium,* Bryant. This organism appears to have been turned so the concave side is up. The flagella appear to orignate from a disklike structure.

g. *S. ruminantium,* Bryant. This individual shows a single variant flagellum, which might be labeled curly, in addition to the normal flagella. This was the only flagellar variant observed in all the slides examined. The wavelength of this curly flagellum is 1.2 microns.

h. *S. ruminantium,* Bryant. The several flagella which can be seen emanating from the soma are twisted into a single strand.

i. *S. ruminantium,* Bryant. Flagella of two organisms twisted together. What else could it be?

j. *Selenomonas* sp. Organism stained directly from water of the DuPage River in Illinois.

k. *Selenomonas* sp. Organism stained directly from the intestinal content of a dog. Note the smaller somatic size of this organism compared to *S. ruminantium* and the strain from the DuPage river.

l. *Spirillum* (*Selenomonas*) *sputigenum,* Macdonald. The flagellar arrangement and wavelength classifies this organism as *Selenomonas.* The soma is smaller than that of *S. ruminantium* and comparable to that of the organism from the dog intestine.

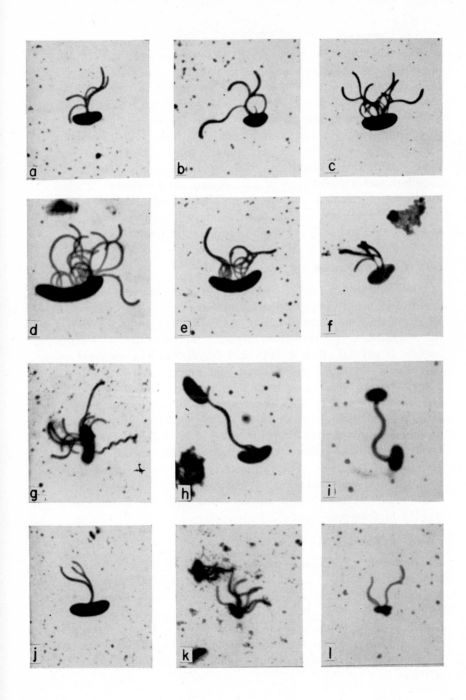

155

The flagella originate as a tuft from the concave side of the organism. In some individuals the flagella appear to originate from a single point while in others the origin is more diffuse. Sometimes only a thick, solid appearing, structure is seen which probably represents several flagella twisted together. The flagellar wavelength was somewhat variable and very long, averaging about 4.0 microns. In all the slides examined only one organism was seen with a single flagellum of shorter wavelength. This curly flagellum had a wavelength of 1.2 microns. The organism labeled *Spirillum sputigenum* appears somewhat smaller than the organism from the cow rumen and the one seen in river water, but of about the same size as the one from the dog intestine.

60. Caryophanon

Only one motile culture of this genus was obtained for study. A culture labeled *Caryophanon latum* was received from Owen D. Weeks of the University of Idaho. At the suggestion of Dr. Weeks the organism was cultured in peptone media with 1% sodium acetate at pH 7.6. Best growth and flagellation was obtained on agar slants. In the liquid medium the growth was rather light. Flagella stains were made from agar slants incubated at 20, 30, and 37° C. Best flagellation was found at 20° C., almost as good at 30° C., but definitely poorer at 37° C. Good motility was not observed in any of the cultures in spite of good flagellation. During the period the culture was studied only the smooth phase of growth was observed. The organisms were mainly short, ovoid rods, frequently arranged in short chains or irregular groups. Only occasionally were seen the longer forms with the characteristic banded appearance.

FLAGELLAR CHARACTERISTICS

Numerous peritrichous flagella were observed at incubation temperatures of 30° C. and below. Most frequently the flagella were normal in curvature but individuals with curly flagella were common (Fig. 67). Individuals with both normal and curly flagella were occasionally seen. Change of pH of the bacterial suspension did not change the wavelength of the flagella. The normal flagellar wavelength averaged 2.14 microns, and the curly 1.09 microns.

156

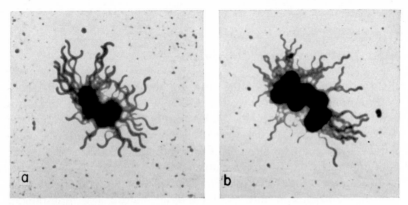

Fig. 67. a. *Caryophanon latum* showing typical peritrichous flagella of normal curvature.

b. *C. latum* from the same culture as in a showing mainly curly flagella with a few normal flagella.

61. DuPage River Organism

In the early course of the study of the flagellation of the bacteria in the DuPage river west of Chicago a most unusual organism was observed. In flagella stains directly from the water the organism appeared as a large rod, usually curved, often in a semi-circle, and sometimes straight. From the soma protruded numerous spines, much like toothpicks stuck into a wiener. A typical organism is illustrated in Fig. 68f. Typical flagella were never seen on these organisms and their bacterial nature was questioned. After considerable effort the organisms were isolated in pure culture and were found to be flagellated with predominantly polar monotrichous flagella. The flagella are typically very long with relatively short wavelength, averaging 1.37 microns. To date the organism in pure culture has not developed the spines so characteristic of the organism in the river water. The identity of the flagellated and the spined forms was established by the observation of spined forms with the typical flagella in the original enrichment cultures made by adding small amounts of various nutrients to the river water. Only in these mixed cultures of bacteria, protozoa, and algae have the organisms been seen with both spines and flagella on the same individual. The organisms vary greatly in size and are typically capsulated. In certain media and under certain cultural conditions branching forms may be seen. What is the nature and function of the spines remains to be determined.

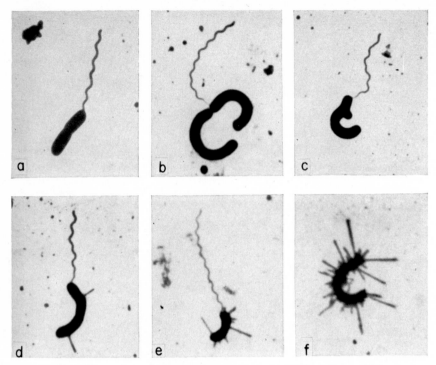

Fig. 68. a. A typical organism as seen in broth culture. Polar mono-trichous flagella.

b. This picture is from a mixed culture in a very dilute medium. The curved soma is very characteristic under such conditions.

c. The organism illustrated shows a short branch. Other and more branched individuals were also observed in some media but most of these were nonflagellated.

d, e. The two organisms illustrated show the spined soma and the characteristic polar flagellum. Both spines and flagella were only observed in the mixed cultures obtained by adding small amounts of nutrients, such as yeast extract, to the river water.

f. The typical spined but nonflagellated form seen in river water. The soma was typically curved, often in a semicircle. The nature and function of the spines has not been determined.

62. *Appendix*

MIXED FLAGELLATION

Cultures of bacteria in which are constantly found individuals with both polar and lateral flagella are not common. A typical example was illustrated in *Chromobacterium*. Another example is that of an unidentified organism from water illustrated in Figs. 69a to 69f inclusive. In this mixed type of flagellation the polar flagella have invariably shown a greater wavelength than the lateral flagella. If the wavelengths were the same the phenomenon would probably be overlooked and the organisms regarded as of the ordinary peritrichous type.

FILAMENTS OF POLAR FLAGELLATES

Filamentous mutants of polar flagellated bacteria may have the appearance of peritrichous flagellation. If the cellular units in the filament are long and the organism is polar multitrichous or lophotrichous, the true nature of the flagellation is usually obvious. Tufts of lateral flagella at regular intervals is not characteristic of peritrichous flagellation. An example of this type is shown in Fig. 69g. Other examples are the *Pseudomonas* sp. illustrated in Fig. 9s and the *Lophomonas* illustrated in Fig. 16c. If the cellular units in the filaments are very short the true nature of the flagellation may be difficult to recognize.

Filaments of polar monotrichous organisms may be very difficult to recognize for what they are. In Figs. 69h and 69i are illustrated the nonfilamentous and filamentous form of an unidentified, nitrogen-fixing, soil organism. This organism was originally described in the literature as peritrichous or showing mixed flagellation with a polar flagellum which appeared to be thicker than the lateral flagella. This culture was obtained and, on plating, both rough and smooth colonies were found. The smooth colonies were composed of polar monotrichous short rods, illustrated in Fig. 69h. The rough colonies were composed of long and short filaments with flagella which had the appearance of being peritrichous. A short filament is illustrated in Fig. 69i. In pure form this filamentous mutant might be difficult to recognize for what it is.

Reference has been made in the preface to the flagella on protozoa and algae. The author has not studied these organisms in detail using flagella staining techniques. With many of these organisms fixation techniques different from those used with bacteria have to be employed not to damage the soma. The typical appearance of flagella of algae is illustrated in Fig. 69j showing *Chlamydomonas* sp. This type of flagella is similar to the undulant flagella found on some bacteria. Protozoa such as *Trichomonas* have the same type of flagella. The typical helical flagella found on bacteria evidently are not characteristic of the flagella on protozoa and algae. The organism shown in Fig. 69k is unidentified but definitely nonbacterial. Except for the long wavelength of about 6 microns the flagellum is very similar to those on some bacteria. In Fig. 69l is illustrated a most unusual(?) and interesting type of flagellation on a protozoan or algal organism. Ciliated flagella of the type shown may not be so unusual if proper staining methods are used.

FIG. 69. a, b, c , d, e, f. Mixed polar monotrichous and peritrichous flagellation.

Note the longer wavelength of the polar flagellum. In f the polar flagellum is missing. This organism was isolated from water, showed a cream colored or slightly yellowish growth on agar, and was nonfermentative. If regarded as peritrichous it could be classified as either *Achromobacter* or as *Flavobacterium*. If regarded as polar flagellated it would be classified as *Pseudomonas* or *Xanthomonas*. Mixed flagellation poses a difficult taxonomic problem but fortunately it is rather rare.

g. This illustration shows two short filaments of a basically polar multitrichous organism. It may be mistaken for a peritrichous type but such types rarely show several flagella originating from one point on the soma as in the illustration. This organism was stained directly from river water.

h, i. These two illustrations are of a nitrogen-fixing organism received from E. Gray in England. The short filament shown in i is a mutant of the polar monotrichous organism illustrated in h. In pure culture the filamentous form could readily be mistaken for a peritrichous type.

j. *Chlamydomonas* sp. Note the undulant and somewhat irregularly shaped flagella.

k. An unidentified, nonbacterial organism from water. Except for the long flagellar wavelength the flagellum is not unlike some found on bacteria.

l. A nonbacterial organism from water with a most unusual (?) type of flagellation. The trunk of the flagellum has the typical undulant shape. The cilia-like structures covering the flagellar trunk are not artifacts.

162

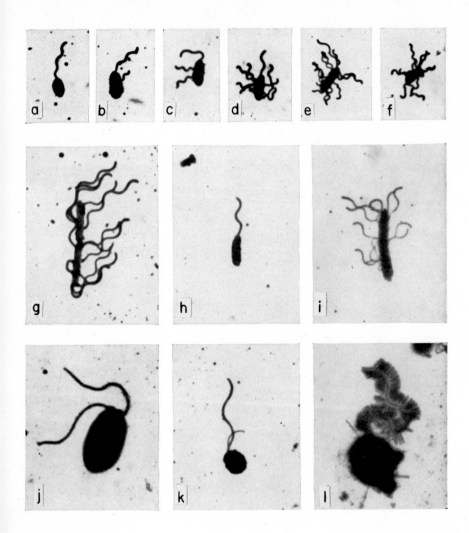

Index

Names of genera are set in bold face, as are page numbers indicating first page of the chapter dealing with the genus.

165

pantothenicus, 129
pasteurii, 124, 126, 129
polymyxa, 124, 129
pulvifaciens, 129
pumilus, 124, 129
sphaericus, 126, 128, 129
stearothermophilus, 124, 129
subtilis, 124, 129
technicus, 129
Bacterium *tardicrescens,* 38
Bartonella, 152
 bacilliformis, 152, 153
begoniae (Xanthomonas), 39
beijerinckii (Clostridium), 136, 139
berta (Salmonella), 113
Bethesda *(Escherichia),* 99
bibula (Cellulomonas), 96, 97
bifermentans (Clostridium), 132, 139
blegdam (Salmonella), 113
bookeri (Alcaligenes), 26, 27
bookeri (Pseudomonas), 26, 27, 32
Borrelia, 148
 novyi, 148, 149
 vincentii, 148, 149
botulinum (Clostridium), 132, 138
bredeney (Salmonella), 113
bronchisepticus (Alcaligenes), 90, 91, 93
budapest (Salmonella), 113
bullata (Mycoplana), 40, 41
bullata (Pseudomonas), 40, 41
butylicum (Clostridium), 134, 139
butyricum (Clostridium), 134, 138

california (Salmonella), 113
campestris (Xanthomonas), 36, 39
capitovale (Clostridium), 132, 138
carnis (Clostridium), 134, 139
carotovora (Erwinia), 102, 105
Caryophanon, 156
 latum, 156, 157
cattleyae (Pseudomonas), 32
Caulobacter, 140
 vibrioides, 140, 142
Cellulomonas, 96
 bibula, 96, 97
 perlurida, 96, 97
 rossica, 96, 97
Cellvibrio, 56
 fulvus, 56

vulgaris, 56
centrosporogenes (Clostridium), 132, 138
cereus (Bacillus), 124, 128, 129
cerro (Salmonella), 113
chauvoei (Clostridium), 132, 138
Chlamydomonas, 162
chlororaphis (Pseudomonas), 26, 32
cholerae (Vibrio), 52, 54, 55
choleraesuis (Salmonella), 113
Chromatium, 144
Chromobacterium, 76
 laurentium, 76, 77
 manilae, 76, 77
 violaceum, 76, 77
chroococcum (Azotobacter), 62, 63, 64
chrysanthemi (Erwinia), 102, 105
cichorii (Pseudomonas), 33
circulans (Bacillus), 126, 129
citreum-mobile (Corynebacterium), 82, 85
citreus (Arthrobacter), 86, 87
cloacae (Aerobacter), 100, 101
Clostridium, 131
 acetobutylicum, 131, 136, 139
 aerofoetidum, 132, 134, 139
 aurantibutyricum, 136, 139
 beijerinckii, 136, 139
 bifermentans, 132, 139
 botulinum, 132, 138
 butylicum, 134, 139
 butyricum, 134, 138
 capitovale, 132, 138
 carnis, 134, 139
 centrosporogenes, 132, 138
 chauvoei, 132, 138
 cochlearium, 134, 138
 difficile, 132, 138
 felsineum, 131, 132, 138
 feseri, 132
 histolyticum, 134, 139
 lentoputrescens, 132, 139
 nigrificans, 131
 novyi, 131, 138
 parabotulinum, 134, 138, 139
 pasteurianum, 136, 139
 perfringens, 131
 roseum, 131, 136, 139
 septicum, 132, 138
 sphenoides, 134, 138
 sporogenes, 136, 138

168

169

170